To Ken
with love Bronwyn.

WORKING
·THROUGH·
PANIC

With appreciation to Angie, Carolyn, Eric, Janet, Jill, Karen, Lorrie, Margaret, Martha, Melony, Rossi and Vicki — thank you

IN MEMORY OF DR STEPHEN BAIN

One day I saw a tree
Beside a busy road
Bitumen hugged its trunk
How could it drink?
Traffic rushed past
Fumes poisoned the air
The noise!
I pitied the tree
Who would want to be a tree?

I gazed at the tree for a long time
I watched as the wind blew and its branches swayed
Its leaves rustled, its berries dropped
A bird rested for a moment before flying off
The day was hot, the sun beat down
Who would want to be a tree?

I stared at the tree for a long time
and then I really saw it
It stood proudly
Its branches like open arms embracing the world
The wind blew and within that sound of rustling leaves
It spoke to me

'I am tree', it whispered
'I have no envy for a creek wandering freely through the hills
I have no jealousy for flowers with colors of the rainbow
The sky is not more glorious
The grass more lush, the sea more wild
I don't ask the birds to stay awhile
my berries not to fall
I am who I'm meant to be
I am truly tree

When the wind blows I bend
When the sun shines, I feel its heat
The birds are my friends
I have no sorrow when they leave
I am tree
I'm what I'm meant to be —
I am truly tree'

I looked at the giant before me and was grateful
The tree who was truly tree
Was showing me how to be
The only thing that I could be
Truly me.

Carolyn Baker

WORKING
·THROUGH·
PANIC

Your Step-by-Step Guide to Overcoming
Panic/Anxiety Related Disorders

BRONWYN FOX

Prentice
Hall

Pearson Education Australia
Unit 4, Level 2
14 Aquatic Drive
Frenchs Forest NSW 2086

Publisher: Nella Soeterboek
Managing Editor: Susan Lewis
Cover and text design: Liz Nicholson, design BITE
Typeset by Midland Typesetters

Printed in Australia by McPherson's Printing Group

1 2 3 4 5 05 04 03 02 01

National Library of Australia
Cataloguing-in-Publication Data

Fox, Bronwyn.
  Working through panic.

  ISBN 1 74009 488 3.

  1. Panic disorders. 2. Anxiety. 3. Stress management.
  I. Title.

  616.85223

Every effort has been made to trace and acknowledge copyright. However, should any
infringement have occurred, the publishers tender their apologies and invite copyright
owners to contact them.

Prentice Hall is an imprint of Pearson Education Australia

CONTENTS

Abbreviations

CBT	Cognitive behaviour therapy
GAD	Generalised anxiety disorder
OCD	Obsessive compulsive disorder
PD	Panic disorder
PTSD	Post-traumatic stress disorder
SA	Social anxiety
LOL	Laugh out loud

PREFACE

It is extraordinary how one moment in time can change your whole life. The morning of my first panic attack was like any other morning. The only hint something was amiss was that I had not been feeling well for a few days, but it wasn't enough to prevent me from going to work. Although it was on my mind as I was driving to work. I had stopped at a red light and was waiting for it to turn green when the attack happened. One moment in time and my life as I knew it had changed for ever.

I did what we all do. I panicked. And, as I say, who wouldn't? An electric shock surging through your body, your whole body reacting to the surge and, to make it really interesting, feeling as if you had left your body. I could 'see' me and I could 'see' me reacting. My heart was racing, I was having difficulty in breathing, I felt dizzy and nauseous and everything seemed unreal, including myself! All I wanted to do was get out of the car and run, which wasn't a good idea considering the five lanes of peak hour traffic waiting at the red light, and the other five lanes opposite me, still moving through the intersection on a green light.

Of course, I went to the doctor, and I went to the doctor, and went to the doctor! I had more attacks and was extremely anxious about it happening again, which, of course, guaranteed it did.

I had no idea what was happening to me and, no matter how hard I fought it, I continued to get worse. Although I knew nothing about meditation, I felt that it would be good for me so I followed the 'hunch' and learnt to meditate. But, at that point, I was too confused and too frightened of what was happening to me to appreciate or understand the fundamental principles of meditation, and what it could actually do to help me.

That was in January 1981, three months after my first panic attack. In March of that year I became suicidal — my life as I knew it was being destroyed and there was not a thing I could do to stop it.

I was referred to a psychiatrist, who immediately diagnosed panic disorder. This in itself is extraordinary. I have met so many people who developed panic disorder in the early 1980s and who were only diagnosed in the late 1990s. Here I was, diagnosed within five months of it beginning. The problem was, I did not believe it. I knew I panicked, I knew I was anxious, but I kept thinking if only my psychiatrist would do something to stop the sensations there would be no need for me to panic or be anxious. After all, I was a credit manager, and credit mangers don't develop 'panic disorder'. 'This is not me. I'm not like this.'

My doctor had prescribed tranquillisers within a few weeks of my first attack, but they did not stop the ongoing horror of my experience. Even when my psychiatrist changed the tranquillisers it kept on going. I could not understand why he couldn't just wave a magic wand and stop the sensations in their track. After all, he was a psychiatrist and isn't that what they are supposed to do?

As my disorder developed, I began to have difficulties doing all the normal things I had taken for granted. Getting to work, and actually staying at work, became a major problem. I would try and drive to work, sometimes I would make it and other times I couldn't. If I couldn't, I would leave my car on the side of the road or in the company car park and catch a taxi home. If I got to work, sometimes I could stay there, other times I would need to go home again. Sometimes after only five minutes! And these times became almost a daily event.

By November 1981 I was for all intents and purposes housebound. I could only travel to the local hospital to see my psychiatrist and to go to the accident and emergency department, when my attacks and anxiety became all too much. Thankfully, the hospital was only five minutes away!

Because I was not 'like this', I didn't tell my psychiatrist. He knew I had left work, but he didn't know that I couldn't do any of the other normal things I used to do. I just kept hoping that it would all go away, that I would wake up one morning and, like the darkness of the night, it too would be gone. That didn't happen.

I knew when I commenced therapy that it was going to be for a limited time, as my psychiatrist was not going to be available in the new year. Therapy finished, and I stayed home except for the visits to accident and emergency or my doctor.

Being housebound didn't mean an end to my attacks or my anxiety. They kept on keeping on, and I lived and breathed them all day, and would be woken from sleep with an attack at night.

I began to meditate every day. Not because I thought it would help me — at that point I didn't think anything could — but rather I used meditation as an escape, from the nightmare I was living. What I didn't know was that meditation is the oldest cognitive technique in the world. While I thought I was escaping, I was actually learning. Learning how to recover.

I would sometimes experience an attack in meditation, but I learnt not to care about these attacks. They were exactly the same as what I experienced during the day, and also at night, but within the quiet of meditation, I learnt to let them happen. I didn't resist them as I normally did. Nor would I become caught up in my thoughts about them. The attacks would flash through me and be over within thirty seconds. As I was not getting involved in my thoughts about the attacks, I felt no anxiety. I learnt that once they were over I would move into the deeper stages of the all encompassing quiet beauty of meditation. And that was all I wanted.

Gradually, I began to understand exactly what I was doing. I realised that I could learn to manage my daily attacks and anxiety in the same way as I did in meditation. I didn't need to spend my life sitting in a chair or on the floor meditating to get relief.

I had learnt to become aware of my thoughts during meditation, and so I learnt to become aware of my thoughts during the day. By doing this, I saw for the first time how they were creating so much of my distress. I saw how my thoughts were actually turning on my anxiety and panic. The more I saw this, the more I realised why there was nothing to fear. I could see how it was all being created moment to moment. And most importantly, I saw I had a choice in what I thought about. I could choose not to think about anything that was going to keep my anxiety and panic going.

I had also learnt in meditation how not to get involved with my thoughts. I had learnt to let them go. I began to do this during the day. I was aware of my thoughts and I saw I had a choice — either thinking them and feeling anxious, or simply letting them go in the same way as I did in meditation.

I was very aware that I needed to let the thoughts go, and not run from them or hide from them, as I knew that would only generate more anxiety. And so I began the process of being aware and letting go.

In the beginning, I would get caught up in my thoughts continually and my anxiety levels would rise, I would have an attack and I would panic. I would pull my thoughts back, time and again, and I began to become involved in letting them go rather than getting caught up in them.

Meditation had also taught me how to let whatever happened during meditation to just simply happen. I also brought this over into everyday life, and learnt to let my attacks and my anxiety happen without resistance. As I did this, my anxiety diminished and my attacks disappeared within thirty to sixty seconds as they had done in meditation. This for me was amazing, because my attacks could last for over sixty minutes at a time, before I dropped back into a highly anxious state.

I began to drive again. I would make it to the bottom of the street before I would turn around and head home, driven by fear, panic and anxiety. I would get home, get control of it and do it all over again. Then I was able to drive half a mile before heading home in total panic. Then I was able to drive one mile, five, ten, twenty. My skills increased and I learnt I could have an attack anywhere, any time, and I could control it by letting it happen and by letting my anxiety just be there. 'So what!'

During this time, I began to see recovery as a process and I learnt to trust the process. I would make gains, only to be thrown back into panic and anxiety in the next hour or the next day. I learnt to understand why this was happening and I learnt to work with it rather than against it. My recovery gained momentum and I began to experience days of freedom that I did not think were possible.

I was still taking tranquillisers, and I decided that the time had come for me to go 'solo'. I withdrew from them and my attacks, panic and anxiety knew no bounds. No matter what I did, I could not get control, and again I saw my life dissolve into fear, anxiety and panic. In those days, tranquillisers were thought not to be addictive. I was told by my doctor that it was my disorder and that, no matter what I did, I would never recover from it. I had worked so hard to get my life back together again, and to be told it was all in vain was too much for me to bear.

This was in 1984. I became suicidal again. Thankfully, my psychiatrist was returning to the local hospital and he confirmed that my medication was addictive, and that my symptoms were those of drug withdrawal. I began a more structured withdrawal program under the supervision of my doctor. I was able to draw on the skills I had learnt, and I was able to let the withdrawal symptoms happen and not become caught up in my thoughts about them. And slowly and surely I recovered.

The one question I had that I could not find an answer for was: Why was I still having attacks? I was no longer frightened of them and I no longer panicked or felt anxious about them. At this stage of my recovery, I was very aware of my thoughts and there appeared to be no reason why these attacks 'without the panic' were happening. All my doctor and psychiatrist could do when I asked the question was to look at me in a slightly bemused way.

And so I continued to recover, with the odd attack without the panic, which really was odd! I returned to work and became a credit manager again, and I continued in therapy with my psychiatrist for a few more months.

At nights and weekends I began to teach other people who also had a panic disorder how to have an attack without the panic, and how not to be anxious about them. In those days very few people were diagnosed as having a panic disorder. At best they were told they had agoraphobia, but the usual diagnosis was 'stress' or 'nerves'.

A few of us established an association for people with an anxiety disorder and it grew very quickly. Carolyn, our poet in residence, joined the association and helped me with the ever-growing workload. Together we survived the ongoing lack of funds and resources, and the ever-growing number of people who wanted our services. I continued to teach other people how to have an attack without the panic, and I continued to ask why is this so. No one could answer me.

I had seen a relationship between my attacks and various meditation states, but I could not find the missing link as to how this could be. In the early 1990s, I was invited to speak at a conference about meditation in the United States. A different conference was being held a week later in the same vicinity and, as I was already going to be in the States, I had registered to attend. One of the speakers, a recognised psychiatrist in dissociation, was presenting a paper about dissociation and panic attacks. I wasn't really sure what he was to speak about, but I thought it would be interesting.

He gave me the answer to my question. His paper spoke of dissociative states, including depersonalisation and derealisation. These states are a feature of spontaneous panic attacks. Depersonalisation is the experience of feeling detached from the body, and derealisation is the experience that nothing seems real, including yourself. Dissociation is also described as trance states or altered states of consciousness and this was my missing link. I saw very clearly that my attacks without the panic were the results of me, unknowingly, moving into a self-induced trance state. Was I excited or was I excited!

And so began a number of years of research with colleague, Jasmine Arthur-Jones. We found that many people who experience spontaneous panic attacks actually dissociate first and then panic as a result of the sensations and feelings of the trance state. We also found that the experience of the 'electric' shock, or burning heat, and other sensations come as part of the trance states. Once we lost our fear of our dissociative states, we no longer panicked! All we were left with was an occasional 'attack without the panic'!

Over the years I have seen the growing understanding of anxiety disorders, although the link between dissociation and spontaneous panic attacks is still rarely considered.

As the understanding of the disorders has developed, there have been many major changes in recognition and treatment of the disorders. Many more people are now being diagnosed either on first presentation to their doctor, or within a few weeks of their first panic attack. And more people now have access to effective treatment.

One of the biggest changes is access to information and resources. In the past these were almost non-existent. Now, with the Internet, people can access information, and lots of it, at the click of a mouse.

After leaving the association, Jasmine and I established a website. The number of people contacting us via the website grew daily. During lunch one day, a workshop participant suggested setting up an email support group to help us meet the requests for email advice and support. I was somewhat hesitant as I was not sure how it could work. I knew from experience that any support group needed to be facilitated. This enables people the freedom to work towards recovery at their own individual pace.

The email support group was established and Vicki, now our group facilitator, offered to assist. The group began online in September 1999. We restricted the group to people who were using the techniques outlined in *Power over Panic*. Restricting the group in this way enabled us to provide ongoing support to people who already had knowledge of the techniques, and this way we could focus specifically on the steps towards recovery.

Initially, it was a learning curve for all of us and over the first few months we 'fine tuned' our approach to working in this medium. The group continued to grow and Vicki became its facilitator. This enabled me to concentrate on the website and on running workshops.

My publisher had commissioned two books, the new edition of *Power over Panic* and a workbook based on the new edition. I had already done the first draft of the workbook. As I began to settle into writing the new edition, I went through the group emails looking for a reference I had made in one of them. No easy task as there can be a hundred emails a day!

But as I was going through the emails I realised — here was the workbook! Email after email showed the recovery process in such an intimate personal way. The emails showed the struggle, the fear, the frustration, the confusion. They also showed the 'light bulb' moments, the triumphs, the power and joy of freedom being regained step by step. The detail in the emails went way beyond any theory about recovery from an anxiety disorder. They told it like it is, and how it is, in graphic detail.

I know from both personal and professional experience that working through to recovery can be difficult and confusing. This can be further complicated by the lack of trust and confidence people have in their own ability to recover. Many people ask for a guide, a 'road map' through the recovery process. As I was reading the emails, I realised that this is what this book could become. A guide which demonstrated the recovery process and the most common difficulties and obstacles people experienced.

I asked a number of group members if I could use some of their emails for *Working through Panic*. Without hesitation they all agreed and all commented that 'if it was going to help other people, yes, I could use them'. So out went most of the draft and in came the emails!

Group members who have contributed to this book come from all walks of life and from a number of different countries. Their ages range from early thirties to sixty-five years. Some have been with the group for a year or more, others have joined more recently.

CONTRIBUTING GROUP MEMBERS

Group members	Country	Age	Anxiety disorder	Time frame (years)
Vicki (Group facilitator)	Australia	40s	Panic disorder/agoraphobia	20
Martha	USA	40s	Panic disorder/agoraphobia	3
Karen	USA	30s	Panic disorder/agoraphobia	1
Angie	USA	53	Panic disorder/agoraphobia	5
Melony	Australia	59	Panic disorder/agoraphobia	30
Jill	Australia	40s	Panic disorder/agoraphobia	15
Margaret	Australia	45	Social anxiety + generalised anxiety disorder	25
Lorrie	USA	40s	Panic disorder/agoraphobia	10
Eric	Netherlands	41	Obsessive compulsive disorder + panic disorder	30
Janet	Australia	65	Generalised anxiety disorder	50+
Rossi	Singapore	30s	Panic disorder/agoraphobia	5+
Carolyn Barker (Poet in residence)	Australia	40s	Social anxiety /agoraphobia	28

Everyone is at various stages of the recovery process, and their emails show their step-by-step progress. In some instances the emails are not in sequential order. I have used some of the emails to highlight various points throughout the book.

While I use the first names of contributing members, some emails are headed simply 'group member'. This has been done to protect the privacy of the members when personal issues are discussed.

None of the contributing members are taking medication. This was by accident more than design. I knew that some members were not taking medication, but I didn't know if others were. As I was finishing this book, I emailed contributing members to ask them if they were taking medication. As I want this book to show the process of recovery as it actually is for individual people, I also wanted to be able to say directly how many group members were taking medication.

Within the main online group we have some people who are also using medication and other people who aren't. Medication can sometimes be very necessary. I needed to take medication. I know personally and professionally how horrific the disorders can be. Medication can reduce the overall levels of distress, and enable people to begin to learn the necessary panic anxiety management skills. This will enable them, ultimately, to manage their panic and anxiety by themselves.

For many of us, though, the recovery process doesn't stop at panic anxiety management skills. Although I run workshops to teach people how to do this, overall the biggest issue in recovery becomes a question of self. Of finding the answer to the lifelong question of 'Who am I?'

Recovery is much like peeling an onion. It can sting and make us cry. Mindfulness meditation teaches us how to work with our obvious and 'loud' panic anxiety thoughts, and it teaches us how to control them. As our mindfulness skills develop, we begin to see the more subtle 'hidden' layers of thoughts that drive so much of our anxiety and depression. These thoughts all revolve around 'who we think we should be' and our need for constant approval from everyone else.

Being 'who we think we should be' means that any sense of self and sense of identity is gained externally. It is not centred within ourselves. As we see these more subtle layers of thoughts, we also see that our anxiety can become our teacher. It can teach us about us, and it can show us how to become who we could be. If we heed its message, we find the answer to the question of 'Who am I?' And our sense of self and sense of identity shifts and becomes centred within us.

The issues relating to a healthy sense of self are overlooked in most anxiety disorder treatment strategies and, in some, they are discounted altogether. The various theories of anxiety disorders see them as a chemical imbalance or learnt behaviour. One therapy targets one aspect, another a different one. Even when combined, they do not provide a holistic treatment approach.

While treatments can medicate and CBT the disorders away, or partially away, people are still at risk of further episodes of their disorder because, overall, the inner conflict remains. And that inner conflict revolves around the question 'Who am I and who should I be?'

In the past, people with an anxiety disorder were considered the 'worried well'. Even today, while this term is not used, the ongoing struggle that people experience is not acknowledged for its profundity and depth of meaning.

All of us who have recovered now realise the significance of this struggle.

Despite the destruction of our lives through our disorder, everything that was taken away from us during this time has been given back to us in ways we never dreamt of. The freedom and the joy to 'simply be' who we are. And there is no greater gift than this.

All because of one moment in time.

CHAPTER 1

'TRULY NOT ME!'

From: Martha

SUBJECT: EXPOSED

I know now that my greatest fears were in being 'found out'. Being exposed as being less than perfect. Somehow feeling fraudulent all the time. I realise that even the closest people around me didn't really know the real me. How could they, when I didn't even know the real me? It is frightening to finally be forced to see yourself for who you really are, not who you think others expect you to be. For me it has been a difficult discovery in many ways. I always thought I could handle the world, and here I am barely able to leave the house.

From: Karen

SUBJECT: EXPOSED

I agree. My 'core' fear is being rejected and abandoned. I think our panic and anxiety are internally driven. We do have a fear of being exposed to other people, as being the inferior person we believe we are. It's a fear of being found out, and then rejected, labeled as unlovable, and ultimately abandoned. This is true, I believe, for all anxiety disorders.

Because of this fear, we take on all the behaviours that lead us to develop an anxiety disorder: passivity, people pleasing and approval seeking. We take on the role of the good 'little boy or girl' who never cause any trouble, and in so doing invalidate our true self. By the time we've reached our late teens or our adulthood, these behaviours begin to backfire.

If you really think about it, we fear being embarrassed by an attack. But why? Because we fear it will lead to rejection and ultimately to abandonment. If we are 'crazy', not only are we out of control (yikes! we must be in control!), we will be 'different' from our families, from our friends, and once again, we feel we will be rejected and abandoned. Going crazy, getting sick, being different, having an attack, is in our minds 'rocking the boat'. And as children we learnt that to rock the boat meant risking abandonment.

I think our anxieties are distractions. We use them subconsciously to keep us focused on the disorder, so that we will not have to face deeper self issues.

From: Bronwyn
SUBJECT: EXPOSED

Trying to be all things to all people takes an enormous amount of energy. It also takes an enormous amount of strength to continually hold ourselves back. To not show our feelings, to not feel our feelings. To always be pleasant, smiling, helpful. To take responsibility for everyone else, and to make sure we do all the above perfectly!

I see our disorders as a 'wake-up call' and the alarm is now so loud we can't roll over and go back to sleep.

From: Vicki
SUBJECT: EXPOSED

For one reason or other, back in those early years, we learnt that expressing our feelings, doing what we wanted to do, was not acceptable or 'safe'. So we put the brakes on our emotional development, to ensure that we fitted in, and would be loved and cared for.

In many ways we are still connected to those early years. We still look at things from the viewpoint of the past, and this isn't appropriate now. In fact it does cause so much of our anxiety and depression.

But we are adults now, and we can look after ourselves. It is safe to be ourselves. The problem is we have forgotten how.

We have forgotten how to be ourselves, haven't we? Martha speaks for so many us when she says, 'I don't even know the real me.' Even before our anxiety disorder developed, we have never known our real self, or ever felt a sense of who we are. Our identity is based on the roles we assume in our life. We are wife, husband, father, mother, daughter, son, friend, work colleague. We are a nurse, a carpenter, a truck driver, a school teacher, a receptionist, a waiter, a company executive, a secretary. Our identity is based on our own, and other people's, expectations and perceptions of who we think we should be. As a result, our sense of self is 'externally' based rather than centred within us.

While we can have the love of our partner, family and friends, many of us know the sense of disquiet within ourselves. That we are not who we appear to be. As Karen and Martha say, we do feel inferior and we do worry that we will be 'found out' and exposed as being less than perfect.

As our anxiety disorder develops we are thrown back within ourselves, and we feel as if there is nothing within us to give us the strength and support we need. There is. We just don't recognise it or know how to find it.

The development of a sense of self is an ongoing process throughout our lives. Unknowingly, we have stopped this process. As Vicki says, we have 'put the brakes' on our emotional development, and in doing so we have been unable to develop a sense of self. A sense of who we are.

Intellectually and physically we have matured, but emotionally we are still relating to people and the world around us as we did in childhood. This is not to say we are childish; it means we have never learnt to express our own thoughts, emotions, ideas and creativity. In essence these are the building blocks of our sense of self and our identity. Without them there is no internal frame of reference and our self-esteem and sense of worth are centred on other people's perception of us.

Our anxiety disorders are a 'wake-up call' from our self to take our 'foot off the brakes', so that we can allow our emotional development to unfold and become equal to that of our intellectual development. Many of us can actually see the difference between our intellectual understanding and our emotional understanding. This is particularly so in relation to our anxiety disorder. We may realise at an intellectual level that our panic attacks and anxiety will not hurt us, but emotionally we struggle with this under-standing and continually become caught up in our panic and anxiety fears.

This is why it is so important that we do release the brakes, so that we can learn to understand, on an emotional level, why we have nothing to fear from our attacks and our anxiety. When we can do this, we recover. And if we continue to allow our emotional development to unfold, not only will we recover but our identity will become centred within our self. We are then safe within ourselves to be ourselves, instead of being who we expect ourselves to be.

Self-esteem

There is very little recognition of the importance of the role that self-esteem plays in the recovery process from an anxiety disorder. From my experience in working with so many people who have a disorder, it is one of the key components to permanent recovery. Healthy self-esteem and anxiety disorders are mutually exclusive. With a healthy sense of self, there is no separation between our intellectual and emotional understanding. And this integrated understanding cannot be dissolved, either by panic attacks or anxiety.

I have always taught that recovery from an anxiety disorder is the loss of fear of our attacks, our anxiety and our fears. Lose the fear and we lose the disorder. When we first develop them, we perceive them to be life threatening, a threat to our sanity or a sign we are about to lose control. In reality, they are a panic attack or symptoms of high anxiety. Nothing more.

There is no dispute that they can feel very violent, but they will not harm us in the ways we think they will. Intellectually, we may know this but, emotionally, we don't. Emotionally, it is the way that we perceive them and think about them that causes the harm, and this perception can harm us to the point it can destroy our lives as we knew them to be.

As Karen says, we are very passive people, and this is demonstrated in our passivity towards our disorder. Although we constantly fight our panic and anxiety, we do so in ways that only perpetuate them. As our fears can be all consuming, we are unable to take a more proactive approach and meet our panic and anxiety head on. When our sense of self is centred within us, we are able to draw upon all our inner resources and go beyond our fears. This enables us to take a more effective and dominant stand against them.

The onion

As I said in the preface, recovery is much like peeling an onion. As we work through the recovery process and peel away the layers, we discover these inner resources within us and we find they have been there all along. We just didn't know it!

Often people with an anxiety disorder will say to me that they are weak people and that having an anxiety disorder shows how weak they are. This is not true. Some people have lived with an anxiety disorder for up to fifty years before they were diagnosed or received effective treatment. Living with an anxiety disorder for a few months, let alone fifty years, is an extraordinary demonstration of strength! We are very strong people — in fact, we are too strong for our own good! We simply don't recognise how strong we are. But we will discover this during the recovery process.

When we begin to work towards recovery, we work directly on the immediate cause of our distress. This, of course, is our panic attacks and anxiety, and the many and varied fears we have in relation to these. As we become more aware and skilled in our ability to manage our attacks and anxiety, we see another layer of thoughts and fears beneath the obvious 'loud' ones of our disorder.

We see how we relate to ourselves and to other people. We see that, in almost everything we do, we seek approval from everyone no matter who they are, including the stranger standing next to us in a queue! We also see how these fears about what people think of us now generate so much of our underlying anxiety and panic.

The created self

As Karen says, her core fear was that she will be rejected and abandoned, and most people with an anxiety disorder have identical fears. These fears have been carried over from childhood, along with the behaviours we adopted as children to prevent these fears from being realised. As we have never addressed and resolved them, we are still trying to appease them with behaviours that block our emotional development, which in turn generates our low self-esteem.

Created self	True self
Low self-esteem	*Healthy self-esteem*
Saying yes when we mean no	Saying no when we mean no
Taking responsibility for everyone	Being responsible for ourselves
Taking care of everyone	Taking care of ourselves
Trying to please everyone	Pleasing ourselves in how we care for ourselves

Being responsible for other people's happiness	Being responsible for our own happiness
Taking care of other people's feelings	Taking care of our feelings
Solving other people's problems	Solving our problems
Meeting other people's wants and needs	Meeting our wants and needs
Anticipating their needs before they are aware of them	Anticipating our own needs
Being available twenty-four hours a day	Being available to ourselves
Doing all of the above perfectly	Accepting that we are human
Constantly feeling guilty	Recognising why there is no need to feel guilty
Feeling trapped and suffocated by the above	Feeling free
Wondering why we have an anxiety disorder	Knowing why we did

Do you recognise yourself in either of these lists? Most people with an anxiety disorder will identify themselves as having low self-esteem. And if we look at this list, is it any wonder that we have an anxiety disorder? This is our daily list of things to do in one way or another, and we need to ask ourselves, 'How much strength does this take?' It takes a considerable amount, and this is why I always say we are too strong for our own good!

I realise some people will look at the list for low self-esteem and wonder why this is being called into question. After all, this is how we have been taught to relate to, and to be with, other people. But now, as adults, the behaviours we learnt in childhood are placing us under enormous unnecessary stress and pressure.

From: Karen
SUBJECT: MOTIVATIONS
I was putting all kinds of 'musts' and 'shoulds' and other perfectionist expectations on myself, and I was trying to live up to these self-created standards. Who wouldn't feel pressured if they felt they needed to be perfect to be acceptable.

I have believed that I must always look good, feel good, be good, do good, be pleasant, agreeable, accommodating, and nice to everyone in order to be acceptable and loved. And I'm supposed to do all this without feeling tired. Impossible! No wonder I started to feel anxious and worn out.

When I look at the fears behind my anxieties, they are always related to how I will appear to others and what they will think of me. It's the idea I have that being less than perfect is unacceptable.

I think it's important for us to analyse our fears down to the core. Find out what is driving our fears. Is it really a fear of death, fainting or a heart attack or embarrassment? What's behind these fears? Is it a fear of not being good enough? Not being acceptable? And if you are not good enough, not acceptable, what do you think would result? Rejection? Abandonment?

Where do you think that comes from? What do you do to yourself, expect of yourself, in an attempt to protect yourself from rejection and abandonment? Do you try to please everyone? Try to be perfect? Try to be superman or superwoman? Do you expect yourself to be without feeling, reaction, response? When you do respond, do you invalidate your feelings or fear them? Do you try not to make a scene, make waves, make a mark? As you go through your life, are you trying to be invisible? Did you learn that being quiet in the corner was safer than being yourself, speaking your mind, rocking the boat? It was like that old analogy of trying to keep a big beach ball under water, and the pressure you feel, and the amount of energy it takes to keep it submerged. How exhausting.

What motivates us to behave the way we do? What are we trying to prevent from happening? Why is it so important to prevent it in the first place? In finding our motivation, we find the key to unlocking the driving force behind our disorder. Once we have that, recovery is inevitable.

When we are so wrapped up in the height of panic disorder, with all the physical and mental symptoms, it is harder to see this stuff, and harder to do this work. But once panic and anxiety is no longer a daily issue, you will come to a point where you will need to take a look a little deeper. You will need to get to the roots of the anxiety weed. I think the reason why people relapse, is that they never dug deep enough. They just cut it off at the surface. So dig my friends. You might get a little dirty in the process, but by God, dig!!!

As children we were dependent on the love and security of our parents, however tenuous that may have been. For a variety of reasons, however innocuous, we learnt as children that the expression of our self and our feelings was counterproductive to our need to be loved, to 'belong'.

As children we didn't have the intellectual development to understand perhaps the full meaning of the injunctions, demands and expectations placed upon us. We learnt, sometimes very quickly, that it was not in our best interests to be, or express, ourselves. In response to this we created a self based upon our interpretation of who and how we should be. We became the 'good nice' child and we became the 'good nice' adult.

There is no doubt that, if we do come from an abusive background, these injunctions and demands would have been continually reinforced by this abuse. But even when these statements were counterbalanced by messages of love and caring, the negative messages had much more impact. If the messages of love came after we were 'trying to be good' it only reinforced our conclusion that there was something very wrong with us, that we needed to hide. If people were going to love us, we felt we had no choice but to be who we thought they wanted us to be. With fear, shame and confusion we kept on trying to be good so that people didn't find out who we really were.

Emotions

We learnt that our anger was not appropriate and so we suppressed our feelings of anger — to the degree that some of us have reached the point where any feelings of anger 'magically' disappear without any, or only partial, awareness of them. This results in our passivity, and our passive response to our anxiety disorder.

Our disorder can destroy our lives as we knew them, yet any anger we may feel is directed towards ourselves. Whereas, if it is directed at our disorder we can make great strides in our recovery. Many people are frightened of any expression of their anger, even towards their disorder. They don't recognise that their anger directed towards it is a normal, natural, healthy response.

We also learnt, especially men and eldest daughters, that expressions of sadness and grief were also not appropriate, and like our feelings of anger we suppressed them. This also applies to our spontaneity and our creativity, our intuition and our joyfulness. Again, for a variety of reasons, these too were not considered appropriate and so, like our anger and grief, we suppressed them.

We became the 'good nice person', and good nice people develop anxiety disorders! While there is nothing wrong *per se* in being 'good nice' people, this is not a spontaneous expression of ourselves. It is an image we have needed to create, because we learnt to feel that the spontaneous expression of ourselves was wrong.

Expectations

From: Vicki
SUBJECT: EXPECTATIONS

People can sometimes limit us, by their expectations of us! Especially if we are using other people's sense of values and judgments. If they are satisfied, then we can relax and are satisfied too. Imagine convincing ourselves we could do even more, even when we feel we can, if we need to have everyone's approval before we do it! What a task!

Instead of learning self-responsibility for our thoughts, feelings and emotions, we assumed responsibility for other people's feelings. Instead of learning to express our own opinions we learnt to accept other people's as being the truth. Instead of learning to care for ourselves, we take care of everyone else.

We tried to become the perfect child, the perfect student. As we grew we tried to become the perfect friend, spouse, partner, parent, employee or employer. We became the strong one, the one to whom everyone could bring their problems, their doubts, their fears, their wants and needs. We have always tried so hard to please others, because we need their approval and we need them to like or love us. Our fear of rejection and abandonment has always been there and is the motivation for all that we do, even now as adults.

Like Martha, we do feel fraudulent, and we do worry that one day we will be exposed for not being who everyone thought we were. This fear comes as a direct result of our need to 'create' a self who can please all people, all of the time. In creating this self, we have suppressed our real self and, in this suppression, we have rejected and abandoned ourselves.

The process of recovery enables us to reconnect back to ourselves. The practice of mindfulness enables us to manage and control our panic attacks and anxiety. It also allows us to take our 'foot off the brakes' and allow our emotional development to unfold at a pace we feel comfortable with. As we 'release the brakes', we learn how to treat ourselves with kindness and dignity. We learn to understand and accept ourselves as we are. We learn that taking responsibility for our lives is healthy and extremely empowering, and it enables us to become all we could be. We learn to feel our feelings and how to express them and we also learn to recognise and draw on our own strength. Put these all together and our anxiety disorder doesn't stand a chance!

> **From: Karen**
> **SUBJECT: EXPOSED**
>
> I think we need to learn that it's okay to rock the boat, to be ourselves. We need to learn that the only person we need to please is ourselves, the only approval we need is self-approval.
>
> There is no such thing as security in this ever-changing world. People will leave us, they will move, or die, or just plain up and leave. The only true security is inner security, to be secure within our self. Secure with who we are, and know that we will never abandon our self by invalidating our real self again.

CHAPTER 2

PREVENTION

From: Martha

SUBJECT: IF ONLY

At the time I was developing this disorder I had ordered a set of china. The store called and told me that my order had arrived. My husband went with me to this huge mega mall, the kind that has five hundred different stores under one roof. I was very nervous but, doggone it, I wanted this china. We had to park what seemed to be miles away from the store, and walk and walk in the heat until we hit the mall.

When we finally got to the store, the assistant said we should unbox all of the china, to make sure that everything was in one piece. Immediately, my fear hit. 'Oh my gosh, what if I panic during the unpacking of the seventy-third piece, and I have to run out of the store' sort of thoughts. Naturally, since I was thinking these thoughts, around about the seventy-third piece or so, I began to get those 'feelings'. Since I was new to this disorder, I actually didn't see it as a panic episode, but rather an 'attack of the vapours' or a 'seizure' of some sorts. I grabbed my purse, mumbled something totally incoherent, and ran out of the store, my husband following me, leaving the assistant with all those boxes and the unpaid bill.

Well, I'd like to tell you all that I turned around the next day and went back and bought the china, or that I went out to the parking lot, got a grip and went back into the store. But I didn't. I never did go back, and I still haven't been back. That damn china is probably still waiting for me.

We've all got these stories, and none of us need feel pathetic or embarrassed, it just happened and that is that. No need to beat ourselves up over it. Now though, we are armed with the knowledge that these feelings won't hurt us, regardless of how awful they feel, or how threatening it all seems at the moment.

I wish I had the knowledge back then that I do now. Maybe I would have let the feelings come, and roll through me like a summer storm, bought the china and proceeded on my way home.

Most of us who experience spontaneous panic attacks never forget our first few attacks. We know where we were, what we were doing, the date and the time they happened! The attacks are dramatic, they are powerful and they do feel very physically violent.

Imagine relaxing in front of the television, or having dinner with friends, being at a cinema or theatre, reading a book, driving to work, being at work or being asleep. Without warning, you feel an electric shock, or burning heat, move through your body. Your heart begins to race, you have difficulty breathing, you experience chest pain and left arm pain. You feel dizzy, nauseous and everything seems unreal, as if you are looking through a white or grey mist. You may even feel as if you have become separated from your body, and you are actually looking at yourself. Your body begins to shake and tremble, thoughts race through your mind. 'What's happening to me?' You feel as if you want to run, run as fast as you can, to get away from whatever it is you are experiencing. And most of us 'run' to our doctor or to accident and emergency at our local hospital.

'You're having a panic attack,' says the doctor.

'Yes, of course I'm panicking. Wouldn't you?' you ask somewhat incredulously. 'But tell me what's happening? I am having a heart attack, aren't I? A stroke? Is it a brain tumour, a seizure? It is all right, you can tell me. Please tell me.'

'You are having a panic attack,' repeats the doctor.

A panic attack? How can that be? The experience seems so much more than a 'panic attack'.

'Are you sure?' you ask. And with that comment, the mind games begin.

The 'game' begins

What if the doctor has made a mistake, overlooked something, mixed up the results of the clinical tests? What if it happens again? What if this was some sort of warning? *What* if it happens again? What if it's worse next time? With each thought our fear and anxiety increase. Try as we might, we simply can't stop thinking about it. The attack happens again. The doctor tells us the same thing. Our thoughts race, our fears increase and the cycle of fear, anxiety and panic begins.

Martha echoes all of us who have had panic disorder: 'If only I had known from the beginning, if only I understood from the beginning, the disorder and its effects would not have happened.'

Although there is now far greater awareness of anxiety disorders within the community and within the health professions, we still don't understand what is happening to us. Other than the feelings of panic, the words 'panic attack' do not have any resemblance or similarity to what we are experiencing. We may be told that we have a chemical imbalance and be given a prescription for medication, but our confusion remains. Chemical imbalance or not, how does this 'imbalance' equate to a panic attack?

I remember when *Power over Panic* was first released and a mental health professional was talking to me about meditation. He said to me, 'We [mental health professionals] know what is happening to people with an anxiety disorder. You and your clients only experience it!'

I remember thinking at the time, this is where we are all missing each other. Our doctor and therapist don't hear us, and we don't hear them. And much of this comes down to the two words 'panic attack' versus our actual experience of it.

The explanations we are given about our attacks do not make sense to us. We are told we have a chemical imbalance, or we are suffering from an overactive fight-or-flight response, but these explanations do not adequately explain our experience. And they leave us with enormous doubt and fear that the doctor has made a mistake.

It is difficult not to feel terrified of what is happening to us. We do panic about our attacks, we panic about our panic and we do become anxious about our anxiety. Our thoughts can race this way, that way and every other way in between. We are drawn back time and again into the fear, and back into our expanding cycle of distress. We can go back and forth to our doctor, to accident and emergency departments, we can seek a second and third, perhaps a tenth, opinion and all we hear are the words 'panic attack', 'anxiety'.

We do become embarrassed and ashamed in seeking reassurance from our doctor, because we know our doctor and other people don't recognise the magnitude of our experience. As so many of us say, 'Stop this from happening to me and there will be no reason for me to panic or be anxious.'

While it is normal to be extremely frightened and confused at what is happening to us, we need to break through this cycle of fear. This way we can prevent the possible development of panic disorder or one of the other anxiety disorders. We need to 'arm' ourselves with the knowledge and understanding of what is happening to us. This enables us to let the attack 'roll through us like a summer storm'; and like a summer storm the attack can pass as quickly as it began.

From: Vicki
SUBJECT: RECOVERY BREAKTHROUGH
Karen, when you first developed panic disorder, what do you think you could have done differently to get this breakthrough to come more easily?

From: Karen
SUBJECT: RECOVERY BREAKTHROUGH
At the beginning I could have worked more on acceptance and believing that it was 'just panic and anxiety' and also worked on letting my symptoms happen. Not buying into them instead of putting my energy into trying to make the symptoms go away.

In the beginning of all this, I think it would have made the journey easier, if I had trusted and believed that I wasn't ill or crazy. I could have then put my energy into letting go, instead of working so damn hard to maintain my grip on things.

All-weather protection

Anxiety disorders can be prevented through early intervention strategies. Unfortunately, early intervention strategies are rarely considered in regard to anxiety disorders. Although these strategies are not readily available within the community, there is much we can do to help ourselves to prevent the development of an anxiety disorder.

I have highlighted these strategies below, and these points are discussed in detail in the following chapters.

You will have times when you will feel overwhelmed with feelings of confusion and fear. This is part of the overall experience of panic and anxiety. When you are feeling this way, come back to the checklist on page 17 and see the area/s you need to work on to break through these feelings.

THE UMBRELLA—THE BASICS

- Once we have been diagnosed as having panic attacks, anxiety or an anxiety disorder, we need to make a commitment to ourselves, and our mental health, to gain a detailed understanding of what we are experiencing.
- Build your knowledge of panic attacks and anxiety by asking your doctor to explain to you in detail exactly what is happening to you. Ask your doctor to clarify any points you do not understand. Remember, your doctor may not realise that you do not understand how your experience fits into the words 'panic attack' and 'anxiety'.
- Read as much as you can about panic attacks and anxiety disorders. Talk with your local anxiety disorder association, as they can provide you with information and referrals to anxiety disorder specialists.
- The Internet is a valuable source of information with thousands of websites dedicated to anxiety disorders. Be mindful, though: some anxiety disorder chat rooms and some bulletin boards can give the impression that people need to 'learn to live with their disorder'. Many people are still not aware recovery is possible.
- Recognise that most people have not had access to early intervention strategies and many people have never had access to effective long-term treatment methods. Some people may also have underlying personal issues, which they are not discussing publicly, and these issues can be a factor in maintaining their anxiety disorder.
- Don't take their experiences and their difficulties as indications that 'this will happen to you'. Early intervention strategies will help to prevent this.

EARLY INTERVENTION STRATEGIES

We all need to recognise and accept that:

- the words 'panic attack' and 'anxiety' do not sufficiently describe the overall actual feeling state of our experience.
- this is what a panic attack feels like; this is what extreme anxiety feels like.
- they are not what we think they are.
- people do not die, go insane or lose control through panic attacks and anxiety.
- you will not be the first one this happens to.
- the 'big one' does not happen!
- there is a 'genetic contribution to the development of panic disorder'.

- panic attacks and/or anxiety develop for any number of reasons, including a current or recent major life stress, a build-up of stress, physical illness, influenza or another virus, marijuana or other similar drugs.
- it is not your fault this has happened to you.
- panic attacks and anxiety do not discriminate—they are equal opportunity disorders. They are not a sign of an inherent weakness within you.
- having panic attacks or an anxiety disorder is nothing to be embarrassed or ashamed about.
- you are not alone in this experience. Ten per cent (ABS 1997) of the population also experience panic attacks and anxiety and other people feel exactly as you do.
- this is a confusing and difficult time.

SHELTER FROM THE STORM

- Take time out every day to meditate or to practise a progressive muscle relaxation technique.
- Refuse to join the mind game of 'what if' and its variants.
- Become the umpire of the game by learning mindfulness/cognitive skills.
- Make informed decisions about treatment options.
- Ask your doctor about early intervention strategies and a referral to a cognitive behavioural therapist.
- Recognise that medication is not necessarily an early intervention strategy in preventing the development of an anxiety disorder.
- Recognise that, if you do need medication, you don't need to perceive this as a 'weakness' or failure.
- Before taking any medication become informed of:
  - the expected outcomes;
  - the length of time you will be using medication;
  - when you can expect the medication to become fully effective;
  - possible side effects;
  - the potential for addiction and possible withdrawal or 'discontinuation' (BMJ 1998) symptoms;
  - any possible interactions with other prescribed medications or 'over the counter' medications;
  - any possible risk to the baby just before, during or after pregnancy, or while breast-feeding.

SELF-ESTEEM

- Recognise that low self-esteem undermines the way we deal with day-to-day and/or major life stress, and undermines us in how we manage our panic attacks and anxiety.
- Thinking we are weak, a failure, pathetic, hopeless or helpless is detrimental to our mental health and fuels our attacks and anxiety.
- Being responsible for everyone else, trying to make people happy, solving their problems and always saying 'yes' to everyone is betraying our responsibility to ourselves and will now create additional anxiety and panic.
- Trying to be all things to all people is detrimental to our mental health.
- The need to be perfect in all we do ensures we do not have a 'perfect' quality of life.

Checklist: walking in gale-force winds

Do you:

☐ believe and accept that you do have panic attacks and/or anxiety?

☐ believe and accept that this is what the experience of panic attacks and anxiety feels like?

☐ understand and accept why the fears associated with your panic attacks and anxiety will not happen?

Are you:

☐ thinking, 'This is not me, I am not like this'? Can you see how this creates further anxiety?

☐ confident that your doctor has not made a mistake in the diagnosis or do you feel they have missed something?

☐ confident that you have told your doctor everything that is happening to you?

☐ trying to be the 'perfect' patient?

☐ learning and understanding all you need to know about panic attacks and anxiety?

☐ taking time out each day to meditate or use progressive muscle relaxation?

☐ learning to see the causes of each of your individual panic attacks?

☐ learning to see the causes of your anxiety?

☐ understanding the principles involved in mindfulness or other cognitive strategies?

- [ ] working with these?
- [ ] possibly having side effects from your medication. Have you spoken to your doctor about this?
- [ ] taking the prescribed amount of medication at the prescribed time?
- [ ] Is your commitment to yourself and your mental health your number one priority?

If you have answered 'no' to any or most of the above, what can you do to assist yourself further?

From: Karen

SUBJECT: THOUGHTS

You need to grab the panic and anxiety thoughts by the throat. For example, you think, 'What if I pass out, fall over dead?' The first reaction is to buy into the thought and get anxious. What I do is say, 'Oh give me a break! Have you passed out or fallen over dead before? *No.* How long have you had these stupid feelings? And *nothing* has ever happened. Give it up! Cut out these stupid thoughts and go run your errands.' It's like a 'tough love' approach!! LOL. It tends to work very well for me!

CHAPTER 3

ANXIETY DISORDERS

From: Bronwyn

SUBJECT: THE DISORDERS

It isn't uncommon for us to have bits and pieces of all the anxiety disorders. People with panic disorder can have aspects of social anxiety, obsessive compulsive disorder, some people may have aspects of post traumatic stress disorder, and there is no doubt many of us have ongoing pervasive anxiety!

Before the three different types of panic attacks were introduced no specific distinction was made in the characteristics of them. A panic attack was a panic attack. People with panic disorder were thought to have a fear of 'open spaces' or a fear of 'the market place'. Their attacks were thought to be a phobic response to external situations. No wonder so many people didn't recover!

While treatment of post-traumatic stress disorder does need to be specific to the individual concerned, working through the various aspects of the other disorders comes down to how we are thinking and perceiving it all. Whether it be the fear of having a panic attack, or any other fears we may have, it all comes back to mind games!

As we become more mindful, we will see how our thoughts are creating the different fears and creating the anxiety and panic. We will also be able to see the choices we have — that is, whether or not we become involved in the 'game' or become the umpire of it!

Theories of anxiety disorders

There are three schools of thought as to what is the cause of anxiety disorders.

The *biological model* presupposes a chemical imbalance, but it is not known if the chemical imbalance is either the cause or the effect of the attack (APA 1994). If this was known, everyone would be able to use a specific medication and get on with their lives. As it is now, some people can use most types of medication without any difficulties, other people may only be able to use a certain few, while a number of other people are unable to use any medication at all.

The *psychodynamic theory* looks at causes related to childhood. While this is so, and I have discussed this in the opening chapter, people need other management strategies to deal with their panic and anxiety in the present moment. As people say to me, 'How is working on my past going to get me out of the house today?' Once people have the necessary management skills, working on past issues can become the prevention 'strategy' of a future in which there is little possibility of a return of their disorder. I discuss this further in Chapter 11.

Behaviour theories suggest that anxiety disorders are learnt behaviours, and recovery means unlearning the previous limiting behaviour (APA 1994). This also includes how to 'unlearn' our panic- and anxiety-producing thoughts.

Some people become confused by the various theories and it is possible that when viewed together they form a whole picture of cause and effect (APA 1990). The recovery process can incorporate all three theories. Some people may need to use medication while they develop their mindfulness or other cognitive skills. Once these skills are mastered, some people will then choose to work on any current or past personal issues that are contributing to their anxiety and depression. Ultimately, it is a personal choice in what treatment strategies people wish to use.

Panic attacks

The American Psychiatric Association describes a panic attack as 'a discrete period of intense fear or discomfort that is accompanied by at least four of thirteen physical or cognitive symptoms' (APA 1994). The experience of less than four symptoms is known as a 'limited symptom attack' (APA 1994). These symptoms include:

Palpitations, pounding heart, or accelerated heart rate, 'sweating, trembling or shaking, sensations of shortness of breath or smothering, feeling of choking, chest pain or discomfort, nausea or abdominal distress, feeling dizzy, unsteady, lightheaded or faint, derealisation (feelings of unreality) or depersonalisation (being detached from oneself), fear of losing control or going crazy, fear of dying, numbness or tingling sensations, chills or hot flashes. (APA 1994)

I will discuss these and other symptoms in detail in Chapter 4.

While panic attacks are associated with a number of anxiety disorders, not everyone who experiences a panic attack develops a disorder. Some people may experience one panic attack and never have another. Other people may experience an occasional one, but don't become caught up in the ongoing cycle of fear that so many of us become trapped in.

The American Psychiatric Association identifies three different types of panic attack and the following categories define the relationship between these attacks and the individual anxiety disorders.

SPONTANEOUS (UNCUED) PANIC ATTACKS

This type of panic attack appears to come 'out of the blue', without warning, and is the type of panic attack that is associated with panic disorder. Spontaneous panic attacks are not related to any specific situation or place. They simply happen without any apparent warning, regardless of what we are doing at the time.

SPECIFIC (CUED) PANIC ATTACKS

People who have social phobia, obsessive compulsive disorder and post traumatic stress disorder experience these types of attacks. People with panic disorder usually don't experience them. The attacks are specific to the various fears related to the individual disorder (see below).

SITUATIONALLY PREDISPOSED PANIC ATTACKS

People with panic disorder may experience this type of attack. Some people with panic disorder can be predisposed to panic attacks in certain situations or places, although they are not frightened of the particular situation or place. For example, people may experience panic attacks while driving or asleep. Sometimes they will have them, other times they won't. They are predisposed to attacks while driving or asleep, but the attacks themselves are not in response to any particular fear of driving or of sleep.

People with one of the other anxiety disorders can also experience this type of attack. For example, someone with social phobia may sometimes experience a panic attack while using an ATM machine, while at other times they may not. However, their panic attack is specific to their fear of embarrassing themselves in some way (see below).

Panic disorder

Panic disorder is the fear of having a spontaneous panic attack (APA 1994). Because of the intensity of the attack most people feel as if they are:

- having a heart attack;
- going to die;
- going insane;
- losing control in some way;
- having a stroke;
- suffering from a brain tumour.

Panic disorder is diagnosed when people experience recurring spontaneous panic attacks and are frightened for at least one month or more of having another one (APA 1994). Part of this fear includes a number of secondary fears in association with the major fears listed above. These secondary fears include:

- The doctor has overlooked something in the original assessment.
- The diagnosis is incorrect.
- The clinical test results have been mixed up with another person's.
- A fear of the 'big' attack in which the major fears will happen.
- Not being able to access medical attention if the 'big' attack or other attacks happen.
- Being alone in case the the 'big' attack or other attacks happen.
- Conversely, having an attack in front of people.

Social phobia

People with social phobia fear they will embarrass themselves, or make a fool of themselves, in social situations or in 'performance' situations (APA 1994) and some people may have a fear of blushing.

These fears can occur in any number of different situations, including:

- initiating or maintaining conversations;
- doing everyday activities such as shopping, walking down the street, in an office situation, writing out receipts, photocopying while other people wait to use the machine, using an ATM machine;
- writing or signing documents in front of others;
- eating and/or drinking in front of others;
- being in a crowd;
- public speaking, either professionally or socially.

People may experience a panic attack in any of these situations, and this panic attack is specific to the fear of embarrassing or making a fool of themselves. While many of us can feel anxious in certain social or 'performance' situations, social phobia is diagnosed when the fear significantly disrupts normal day-to-day living.

Obsessive compulsive disorder

The essential features of OCD are ongoing obsessions and/or compulsions (APA 1994). People can be made extremely anxious by one or more of these and their life severely disrupted as a result. While people recognise that their obsessions and compulsions are excessive and/or unreasonable, they are unable to control them no matter how hard they try.

Obsessions are recurring ideas, thoughts, impulses or images and, although they are not based on 'real life' concerns, they do create severe anxiety and panic. Compulsions are a reaction to the obsession and they are used as a way of trying to stop either the anxiety and/or the feared event.

- Obsession: The fear of becoming contaminated by germs, leading to compulsive handwashing and cleaning.

- Obsession: Repeated doubts that electrical appliances have been left on. This can lead to compulsive checking and rechecking to ensure that they are turned off.
- Obsession: A need to hoard everything and anything in case it is needed in the future.
- Other compulsions that can be used in an effort to stop, or prevent, obsessive thoughts include praying, counting or continually repeating certain words.

Post-traumatic stress disorder

PTSD is the result of a severely traumatic experience which involves a life-threatening event, or serious physical injury, either to our self or to a person close to us (APA 1994). These can include:

- major car or other serious accidents;
- victim of physical assault, sexual assault and/or rape;
- armed robbery;
- experiences of war;
- natural disasters such as bushfires, cyclones, hurricanes, earthquakes;
- life-threatening illness.

One of the characteristics of PTSD is the experience of flashbacks and/or nightmares of the traumatic event(s). These can be so intense the person experiences the original feelings and emotions, as if the traumatic event was happening again. People may also have:

- difficulty in falling asleep or have difficulty staying asleep;
- irritability or outbursts of anger;
- difficulty concentrating;
- hypervigilance;
- exaggerated startle response.

People with PTSD may experience panic attacks in situations or places similar to, or reminiscent of, the actual trauma. For example, people who have experienced the devastation of bushfire may have a panic attack on days when the fire danger is high, or if they hear fire sirens. This panic attack is specific to the trauma they experienced during a bushfire.

Generalised anxiety disorder

Generalised anxiety disorder is 'excessive anxiety and worry for at least six months about a number of events or activities' which may or may not happen (APA 1994). This worry can include fears and worries about children, partners, other family members or close friends, a work situation or a specific planned event.

People with generalised anxiety disorder often tell me that they have been worriers for most of their life. This worry can become all pervasive and is accompanied by ongoing physical symptoms.

Agoraphobia

> **From: Martha**
> **SUBJECT: HERCULES**
> I am invited to visit friends in another state. It is a sixty-minute flight, but obviously if it takes a herculean effort for me to make it to the store on the corner, it's pretty doubtful that I am going to get on a plane and fly anywhere. I feel depressed. It feels like it's so stupid having to baby step my way through this stupid condition. It leaves me feeling weak and helpless and stupid, and totally brain damaged. I am just angry that I am wasting my life like this, I am furious and I am pissed off. Does this make sense to you. To anyone???

It makes sense to everyone who has an anxiety disorder! And it makes no sense at all that early intervention strategies for anxiety disorders are not seen as priority within the health system. Why do people develop an anxiety disorder, and the secondary conditions associated with it, when early intervention strategies can MINIMISE or prevent them in the first place?

Many people go on to develop agoraphobia and major depression as a result of their disorder. People can also develop an addiction to, or dependency on, prescribed medication, while other people can develop an alcohol dependency. No, it doesn't make sense at all!

Agoraphobia was known as the fear of open spaces or the 'market place', but now it has been redefined. Agoraphobia is the avoidance of situations and places. People with panic disorder will be anxious and/or avoid situations and/or places for fear of having an attack or anxiety symptoms.

Agoraphobia in social phobia is avoidance behaviour related to social situations. In obsessive compulsive disorder it is avoidance behaviour relating to the particular obsessive thoughts. In post-traumatic stress disorder it is avoidance of 'stimuli' related to the trauma (APA 1994). Although the avoidance behaviour is limited to the specifics of these particular disorders, it can be all encompassing and people may become housebound as a result.

I have always seen our avoidance behaviour in three different ways. The first is an overall defence against further panic attacks and anxiety. Some people begin to avoid situations or places where they have already experienced an attack, because they fear they may have another. Other people begin to avoid any situation or place, whether they have had a panic attack there or not. In the initial stages of the disorder, many of us are terrified and confused by our overall experience and, as a result, we can't do any of the things we would normally do.

Nor do we necessarily place much significance on our avoidance behaviour in the early stages of our disorder. Most of us are just wishing and hoping and waiting for the day that our panic and anxiety simply disappear — 'that it is all just a big mistake'. Or we wait for the miracle drug or miracle cure to take it all away. This, of course, doesn't happen and, by the time we begin to realise that no one will rescue us, our overall 'defence lines' of where we can or can't go are already established. For some people this could mean they are housebound or extremely limited in where they can and can't go, and what they can and can't do. Surprisingly, this can be a shock for many people when they realise how disabled they have become.

This is when the second form of avoidance behaviour comes into play. As we try to move beyond our 'defence lines' the 'what if' thoughts become the dominant player. What if:

- I have a panic attack?
- I can't get help?
- I can get there, but can't stay?
- I can't get away?

- I have the big one?
- I can't get there?
- I can stay, and then suddenly I have to go?
- I can't get home?

- I can't drive?
- people see me this way?
- I faint?
- I can't walk?
- I make a fool of myself?
- I lose control?
- I have an attack of diarrhoea?
- everyone sees me shaking?

- I am trapped?
- I lose control?
- I can't move?
- I can't stand?
- I embarrass myself in some way?
- I vomit?
- I lose control of my bladder?
- I fail?

Our anticipation of everything that could go wrong increases our anxiety to extreme levels and we may have an attack. And so we avoid the situation or place completely as a result of this anticipatory anxiety or panic. Or we do what we need to do with great difficulty and so we don't attempt it again.

The third form of avoidance behaviour is a result of the effects of our anxiety disorder. Some people can have constant nausea, exhaustion, dizziness, feelings of physical weakness and severe headaches. And so it becomes extremely difficult to do what they normally do because they don't feel well enough to do it!

From: Angie
SUBJECT: WHAT IF? — I'VE GOT IT!

I was thinking about the emails and about the 'what ifs'. It suddenly hit me. This is the disorder!! The emails were about morning panic attacks and why they happened. Someone made the comment, 'What if it happens again tomorrow morning?'

I think I finally understand this disorder. It is not the panic attack. It is what we do between the attacks! Bronwyn said this a few weeks ago, and I think I finally understand. It is the 'what ifs' that get us.

I remember the first real panic attack I had this time when it all came back. I was driving to the grocery store and I had a very powerful panic attack when I pulled into the parking lot. I had been having them again for some time, but this was a doozey. I immediately went home and the agoraphobia started again. I was afraid to go to the store or anywhere for fear I would have another panic attack. I suddenly realised that it is okay to have an attack, it is what I do with the fear that keeps me trapped.

Learning to work with our avoidance behaviour is, of course, a major part of the recovery process and I discuss this in detail in Chapter 9.

Depression

As our lives become increasingly restricted through our disorder, many of us develop a major depression in reaction to this. The symptoms of depression can be very similar to those of anxiety and this adds to our confusion and we become anxious over our depressive symptoms.

Even now, many people are still not being diagnosed as having an anxiety disorder, and their secondary major depression is assumed to be their primary diagnosis. This only compounds their confusion even further and can prevent them from accessing effective treatment for their anxiety disorder.

The symptoms of depression can include (APA 1994):

- loss of interest in enjoyable activities;
- irritability;
- changes in appetite;
- lack of concentration;
- sleeping difficulties;
- oversleeping;
- no energy;
- fatigue;
- reduction of sexual interest or desire;
- thoughts of suicide.

As our lives become more restricted through our anxiety disorder, we feel helpless in our ability to 'pull ourselves together'. This only compounds our sense of worthlessness, and some people can begin to have thoughts of suicide. In some instances, people feel very ashamed of these thoughts and find it very difficult to talk about them. People can also be afraid that if they do talk about them they will be committed to hospital.

If you are having thoughts of suicide, don't let feelings of shame or fears of being committed to hospital stop you from asking for help. You have nothing to be ashamed of, nor is there anything to fear by asking for help.

Asking for help is not a sign of weakness or failure. It is an acknowledgment of the degree of your distress, and you can begin to ease this distress by asking for assistance. Speak with your doctor. They will understand and will be able to assist you.

Talk to your family and tell them how you are feeling. If a family member was feeling this way, you would want to do everything you could to assist them. You need to give them the opportunity to help you. You can also speak with a close friend, your local priest or minister, or you can ring one of the crisis telephone services. You are not alone. Help is available for you.

Medication

Our study and others (Arthur-Jones & Fox 1997; Kenardy et al. 1988) show that many people would prefer not to take medication for their anxiety disorder. There is, however, a time and place for medication for some people, especially if they are beginning to have thoughts of suicide. However, medication by itself is not the definitive long-term answer for many people (Otto et al. 1994).

Medication is the first, and sometimes the only, treatment option that people are offered. Some people are prescribed medication on their first visit to their doctor, even though they may have only experienced one panic attack.

If this does happen it is very important that we ask our doctor about other treatment options such as cognitive behavioural therapy. This then gives us the necessary skills, from the beginning, that we need to control our panic attacks and anxiety.

If we decide to use medication, then we need to be able to make an informed decision about it. We need to know exactly what we are taking. So many people who speak to me have no idea of the type of medication they are using. They don't know if it is a tranquilliser or an antidepressant. Nor do they have any idea of possible side effects, or withdrawal symptoms or 'discontinuation reactions' (BMJ 1998).

When we are prescribed medication, we do need to discuss this fully with our doctor. It is our responsibility to ourselves to do this. The following checklist is based on the most common questions I am asked every day about medication.

Medication checklist

- We have the right to discuss any questions and concerns we have about our medication with our doctor.
- There is no reason to feel embarrassed or ashamed about this.
- If you experience side effects and feel unsure about them, speak with your doctor.
- If you are told the new symptom/s is/are part of your disorder, seek a second opinion.
- If you are told you will need to take tranquillisers for longer than a month, seek a second medical opinion.
- If you are told minor tranquillisers have no side effects at all and/or are not addictive, change your doctor.

QUESTIONS TO ASK YOUR DOCTOR

- Why the medication is being prescribed, and how it works.
- What type of medication is being prescribed: tranquilliser, antidepressant, beta blocker, other.
- How long it takes before the medication becomes fully effective.

TRANQUILLISERS

- How long you are to take this medication. Be mindful that tranquillisers can be addictive within two to four weeks (Brayley et al. 1991).
- How long before the medication becomes fully effective.
- What the short-term outcomes are.
- The exact prescribed dose you are to take each day.
- What the side effects are.
- The length of time a single dose is effective.
- The possible withdrawal effects if a single dose is accidentally missed.
- The possible withdrawal effects when discontinuing tranquillisers permanently.
- If there are withdrawal effects, how long they last.

ANTIDEPRESSANTS

- How long you are to take this medication.
- How long it takes for the medication to become fully effective — antidepressants can take up to six weeks.

- What the short- and long-term outcomes are.
- The exact prescribed dose you are to take each day.
- What the side effects are.
- The length of time a single dose is effective.
- Possible discontinuation effects if a single dose is accidentally missed.
- Possible discontinuation reactions associated with antidepressants when discontinuing them permanently.
- If there is a discontinuation reaction, how long it is expected to last.

USING MEDICATION

- Antidepressants cannot be used on a casual basis.
- It is our responsibility to take our medication as it has been prescribed.
- To prevent any possible withdrawal or discontinuation reactions, ensure you have a new prescription filled two days before your current prescription runs out.
- Check with your doctor or pharmacist to see if there are any adverse interactions with other prescribed medications or 'over the counter' preparations such as cold and flu medication or herbal products.
- Women who are considering pregnancy, who are pregnant or are breast-feeding need to speak with their doctor about any possible risk to the baby.
- Don't use alcohol when taking prescribed medication. Speak to your doctor about this.
- Do not just stop using your medication. If you are considering stopping your medication you do need to speak with your doctor about this. Withdrawal of your medication needs to be done gradually over a period of time under medical supervision.

OTHER

- If you have been taking an antidepressant for over six weeks and you find there is no significant improvement in how you are feeling, discuss this with your doctor and ask to be changed to another medication.
- If you are told you will be on medication for the rest of your life because of your anxiety disorder, change your doctor.
- If you only see your doctor for a minimum amount of time every few weeks, ask for a referral to a cognitive behavioural therapist. If you are refused, change your doctor.

- If you are told cognitive behavioural therapy is not recommended, or your doctor tells you it doesn't work, change your doctor.
- If you are told you will be referred to a cognitive behavioural therapist in six months, or a few years, change your doctor.

From: Karen
SUBJECT: LIGHT BULBS

I think I just had an 'ah-ha' moment. A light bulb episode!!

If recovery from panic disorder means having an occasional attack, but going about your business, living your life, not limiting yourself or living in fear, then the only thing separating any of us from full recovery is what we *think* about panic, what we're telling ourselves.

Do people with occasional gallbladder attacks stop living? Do people with asthma attacks stop living? Do people with recurrent migraines stop living? Hell no! They accept these episodes in their lives as par for the course, and just carry on. They don't like it, but they accept it and that's that. So why is panic so different? It's not! *It's not!* I think I finally *get it*!

All my life I have been held back because I have been fearful. Even when I hadn't panicked in years and years, I avoided doing certain things in case I *might* panic. But so what if I do panic? What's the harm? If I don't *care* anymore if I panic or not, then I don't have to avoid anything anymore, don't have to hold myself back. I can go out there and live my life, and panic all over the place if I need to. Big Deal. The ironic thing is, once you don't care anymore, you panic less and less.

I don't have to wait until I haven't panicked in months or a year to consider myself recovered. I don't have to wait until I feel 100% fine before I go back out into the world and make my mark. I've been putting off seeing my friends, putting off dating, putting off *life*. It's the idea that I've got to get rid of this panic stuff before I'm acceptable, before I can get on with life. It's been the fear of embarrassment, what will others think or say if I panic?? Arghhh!! Who gives a hoot what they think? I can live *now*. *Today*. Because if panic is so harmless, and has nothing to do with insanity or competence, if it's not going to make me pass out, throw up, have a heart attack, why the heck am I still tip-toeing through my life? Fear of criticism or rejection?? Who *cares*!

I think I have *finally* grasped the meaning of '*So what*', and it is more profound and deeper than I could have *ever* imagined.

CHAPTER 4

UNDERSTANDING OUR SYMPTOMS

From: Melony

SUBJECT: SYMPTOMS

I would worry and obsess over some physical problem. Then I realised that I am making myself sick with the fear of the anxiety symptoms, and all that it is doing is causing more anxiety symptoms!

I really didn't know about the 'fight-or-flight' response until a year ago, and now it is all starting to make a lot of sense to me. Now I just don't worry about the symptoms anymore, and they will go away if I don't take any notice of them. But it does take a little while to undo thirty years of fear!

From: Angie

SUBJECT: SYMPTOMS

The dizziness was the worst for me. I have found that if I can just relax my legs and my back, the dizziness gets so much better. I used to get so dizzy that I could hardly walk or stand up. It is very scary. Try to notice where you are holding the tension, or what I call resistance in your body. I would tense up so much against the feelings of panic that my body would be just one stiff board!

From: Bronwyn

SUBJECT: SYMPTOMS

It is very important that everybody knows that their symptoms are those of panic and anxiety. Everyone does need to have a full medical check to make sure there is no physical cause for their symptoms, as our symptoms can mimic a number of physical conditions. But once our doctor has made the diagnosis of panic attacks and/or anxiety then we do need to *believe* it. Otherwise, all we will be doing is getting caught up in our fears about them, which just keep them going!

There are infinite combinations of symptoms. We all see this in the group, and I see it in the workshops and in speaking with other people. Some people may have three or four symptoms, other people may have five or six happening at any one time. Other people can have ten or more all at the same time. Some people report they have chest pains, palpitations and extreme headaches. Others will have breathing difficulties, chest pain, diarrhoea, nausea and dizziness. Quite a number of people will have the 'burning red' face, their hands will be visibly shaking and they will perspire profusely.

Some people can have all of these plus others! Many of us fear our panic attacks overall, while other people may focus on one or two of their panic attack symptoms. Some may fear their breathing difficulties, someone else will focus on their chest pain and palpitations or 'missed' heartbeats.

Other people may focus on the fear of having an attack of diarrhoea. Some people will have all these symptoms but worry about something happening in their lives or what they think should happen, shouldn't happen, could happen, must happen!

Vicki said the other day when everyone was talking about the dissociative symptoms that not everyone will have them. And that's right. It is usually the people with panic disorder who do.

Besides the experience of depersonalisation and derealisation, many people will feel dizzy and as if they are going to faint. Some people talk about a tingling burning sensation moving through their body, or of shooting sensations in their neck and scalp. Someone said, in an earlier discussion, they suddenly felt a wave of 'burning hot ice' move through their veins and it made them feel sick.

And, of course, people can have the racing heart, breathing difficulties, the shaking and trembling and a whole variety of other anxiety symptoms as well as the dissociative ones. Some people aren't frightened of their dissociative symptoms but worry about their racing heartbeat. Other people will not be frightened of heart palpitations but will be frightened by their dissociative symptoms.

There is a study which shows people with panic disorder can have different symptoms with every single panic attack (Kenardy et al. 1988), and our research also shows this (Arthur-Jones & Fox 1994). This is part of the reason why we need to have a very good understanding of our panic attacks and our anxiety. Otherwise we will continue to get caught up in it all. And that only creates more symptoms!

Don't we get confused with our symptoms? They can swap, change, come back, disappear and then reappear with a slight variation. I often say in my workshops that, as we seem to be rid of one symptom, ten more are queuing up waiting to take its place. It is just as if the symptoms are standing at the starting gate, jumping up and down and saying, 'Pick me. Pick me, its my turn!'

Working towards our recovery means we do need to understand the various symptom groups. In most treatment programs there is usually no distinction made between these groups. This can cause confusion and it does make it much harder for us to work with it all.

In the workshops, I separate the symptoms into five different categories. This enables everyone to understand how their symptoms are being created. This in turn allows people to target their individual symptoms specifically, which enables them to learn to control the symptoms more effectively.

Fight-or-flight response

The first group of symptoms is a result of the fight-or-flight response. This is a natural response in human and animals that automatically activates in times of danger. It enables us either to stay and fight the danger, or to run from it.

Within moments of us perceiving a dangerous situation, the fight-or-flight response releases adrenalin and other hormones into our body to provide us with the energy we need to deal with the threat. Our heart rate increases, our breathing rate increases, our muscles tense, we begin to perspire. This is the fight-or-flight response in action.

When we have an anxiety disorder, we activate the fight-or-flight response by the way we are perceiving and thinking about our fears or symptoms. Although we may see these as being dangerous, they aren't! But our body can't tell the difference between our 'what if' thoughts and the thought: 'Here comes a truck that's lost its brakes and is heading straight for me.' Our body is doing what it is 'programmed' to do in times of danger.

The problem is we are creating the threat of danger by the way we think. The more we become caught up in our fears, the more our body responds to the threat of 'here comes that truck' and round and round we go.

Hyperventilation

The second category of symptoms leads in from the fight-or-flight response. The effects of our rapid breathing can lead to hyperventilation, which is a decrease of carbon dioxide in the bloodstream. This can be experienced as pins and needles in our fingers and hands, feet and around our mouth. We may also feel faint or dizzy. We can become frightened of these symptoms, and our body responds to our thoughts of 'here comes the truck, again' and we continue to go round and round!

Hyperventilation is not dangerous. Carbon dioxide levels can be increased simply by cupping our hands over our mouth and nose and breathing into them, and then breathing back the exhaled breath. Or we can increase the levels by taking a series of slow deep breaths.

Muscle tension

The third group of symptoms is also a result of the fight-or-flight response. This is the tension we feel in our muscles. We can experience chest pain, left arm pain, jaw pain, pain in our legs and extremely painful tension in our neck and head. And when we fear these, especially the first three, our body responds to the threat of the 'truck' and away we go again!

Dissociation

The fourth group of symptoms are the dissociative ones. Dissociation is also known, as I've said, as 'altered states of consciousness' or trance states. This group of symptoms is mainly experienced by people who have panic disorder or, in some instances, post-traumatic stress disorder. While the ability to dissociate is not taken into account in any of the theories about the anxiety disorders, many people with panic disorder report that the experience of dissociative symptoms is the reason why they panic.

This is confirmed in our research (Arthur-Jones & Fox 1994), in the responses I get when running workshops and by the many emails we receive from our website where this is discussed.

The more 'distinguishable' sensations of trance states include:

• *Derealisation*: a feeling as if we and/or our surroundings are not real, as though we are looking through a white or grey mist or a 'veil'.

- *Depersonalisation*: feeling detached from the body; an 'out of body' experience where people feel as if they are above, or behind, or standing alongside themselves.

Other sensations can include:

- feelings of floating;
- feelings as if our body has expanded;
- feelings as if our body has become smaller;
- feelings as if we are falling into a void;
- oversensitivity to sound; everyday sound and noise is amplified;
- oversensitivity to light, including daylight; increase in depth and brightness of colours;
- oversensitivity to taste;
- oversensitivity to smell;
- oversensitivity to touch;
- visual distortions such as stationary objects appearing to move.

And aren't some of these enough to make anyone panic!

One of the major effects of the alteration in consciousness is a feeling of dizziness. And there is no doubt that those of us who do dissociate experience quite severe dizziness at times. A research paper that links dizziness to depersonalisation theorises that it is not so much what we are doing at the time we dissociate, 'it is the magnitude of the change' of consciousness, that is significant (Fewtrell & O'Connor 1988).

THE ABILITY TO DISSOCIATE

The ability to dissociate usually begins in childhood. Some people with an anxiety disorder do have a history of childhood abuse, and the ability to dissociate enabled them to 'escape' from this abuse. Other people, who do not have a background of abuse, learnt to dissociate in other situations, being at school, for example. People have told me they used to trance out during school lessons that they were not interested in, or disliked.

Evidence suggests that people with the ability to dissociate 'may display high hypnotisability and high dissociative capacity' (APA 1994). While some people are aware of their ability to dissociate, and have always been aware of it, others 'lose' this ability as they grow older. In times of major stress or other forms of stress, this ability can be activated again. Not so much as an 'escape mechanism', but as a result of becoming more 'vulnerable' to the ability to dissociate as a result of the stress.

When we are stressed we can skip meals, we may not feel like eating at all, and we can have difficulty sleeping. This in turn increases our vulnerability to dissociate and one day, without warning, we do!

It is interesting to note that other cultures actually use fasting and sleep deprivation, among other methods, to deliberately induce various trance states. A leading expert in altered states, Dr Charles Tart, comments that many other cultures 'believe that almost every normal adult has the ability to go into a trance state' (Tart 1972). The American Psychiatric Association notes that these states can be an 'accepted expression of cultural or religious experience in many societies' (APA 1994).

Other ways that we can unknowingly induce these states include staring at a book, a computer screen; when we are driving, at the road ahead of us, the traffic light, the car in front of us; when talking with another person. We can stare out of our office window, or as we are walking and staring at a point in the distance. Essentially, any time when we find our gaze becoming 'fixed' on something. Fluorescent lights can also induce these states, so too can intense concentration or deep self-absorption.

From: Martha
SUBJECT: AH HAH!
I think it's interesting to note that the surreal feeling that we have is benign. It's buying into the feeling that causes the actual worry.

Two years ago I was working on a large project. It was at a time where my disassociation was rampant. I clearly remember one horrific episode at the bathroom sink, staring at myself in the mirror for an hour, trying to decide if I was really me, or if I had metamorphosed into someone else. Sounds pretty neurotic and insane, doesn't it?

I had three months to finish the project, and to be honest, I can hardly remember doing it, nor the hours of research that I put into it. One of my friends is a neurologist. I called him up one day and I broke down and sobbed while telling him about my surreal feelings.

He told me that when he was doing delicate surgery, he too would go into a trance state, as he was so focused on the task at hand, so intent on what he was doing, that he shut other things out.

I think what I experienced last week, when I was getting back into driving, was similar to this. I was so intent on doing well, I was working with my thoughts, watching the traffic, watching me, and I was in a trance-like state of pure concentration.

This morning I had errands to run and felt the same feelings, but this time I recognised that it wasn't from tension, hyperventilation, staring for too long, or not blinking. Rather I was thinking too hard about too many things.

In this state of mind, we feel as though we aren't thinking anything, but in fact we are. If we weren't thinking, we wouldn't be feeling anything! LOL. Truly a trance like state of this kind is merely induced by intense concentration. Instead of just 'being', we are stuck in the moment of 'doing', and it takes all of our effort. In time we learn to integrate 'being and doing', and the spacey feelings slink away, as do the other symptoms as well.

NOCTURNAL PANIC ATTACKS

It is interesting to note that research suggests that a 'sleep' panic attack occurs 'during the transition from stage two to stage three sleep' (Uhde 1994). In other words, during an alteration of consciousness. Many people who dissociate report they can also experience an attack as they begin to go to sleep. This first stage of sleep is called the hypnogogic state.

'Sensory shocks' can also accompany the hypnogogic state, or can occur during the transition from dreaming sleep. These were first noted in 1890. Researchers described them 'as an upward surge of indescribable nature, an electric sort of feeling ascending from the abdomen to the head sometimes followed by bodily jerks, or a violent explosion and/or a flash of light' (Oswald 1962).

The researchers also note that a 'sense of alarm', together with a cold sweat, labored breathing and tachycardia often follow' (Oswald 1962). And for many of us this 'sense of alarm' can be the current definition of our feelings of panic!

'SENSORY SHOCKS'

Whether we are awake or asleep, these 'sensory shocks' can also be experienced in conjunction with our dissociative symptoms. From our research (Arthur-Jones & Fox 1994) it does appear that these 'shocks' are induced by dissociative states. These 'sensory shocks' are experienced as moving through the body as:

- an 'electric current';
- a rush of unusual intense energy;
- intense burning heat;
- burning tingling heat;
- a wave-like motion;
- a hot prickly sensation;
- an 'ants crawling' sensation;
- intense cold;
- intense burning cold heat.

Many of us panic as a result of sensations, and the fight-or-flight response is activated. Our study showed that 71% of people who experience this type of attack reported that they find it difficult to link these sensations to that of adrenalin and the fight-or-flight response. The study also showed that 69% of people with panic disorder reported they experienced an attack while going to sleep, and 86% reported that an attack wakes them from sleep. Seventy-eight per cent of people with panic disorder reported experiencing their attacks when they were feeling relatively 'calm' — while watching television, reading a book, relaxing with friends (Arthur-Jones & Fox 1994).

The behavioural school of thought presupposes that, when people are relaxed, they have more time to worry about their symptoms. Not necessarily! When people are relaxed it is very easy for some to dissociate. One researcher commented that the transition into trance states can occur in a split second (Putman 1989), and it is in that split second that we can go from feeling relaxed to total panic.

One particular study surprised researchers when they found a 'paradoxical positive correlation between increases in slow wave EEG and increasing anxiety' while the patient was at rest (Knott 1990). 'Slow wave activity' indicates a very relaxed state. And the question becomes: How can we be relaxed and anxious at the same time? The study concluded that 'replication of increases in slow wave activity in further studies would suggest psychobiological disturbances in panic disorder are not merely normal emotions expressed in inappropriate contexts' (Knott 1990).

'MERELY NORMAL EMOTIONS'?

And this is the point of departure between many professionals and people who experience spontaneous panic attacks. Everyone with panic disorder is well aware that the symptoms of their attacks are not 'merely normal emotions expressed in inappropriate contexts'. By 'normal emotions', the researchers are referring to the fight-or-flight response.

As I said above, some people have a history of childhood abuse and have felt in danger on many occasions because of the abuse. Irrespective of our childhood, many of us with panic disorder have had occasions as adults where we have been in danger. A 'near miss' in a car is a common example. All of us know exactly what the fight-or-flight response feels like. We have all been there.

While the fight-or-flight response is activated moments after we experience an attack, there is no comparison between the precipitating symptoms of our attacks and the fight-or-flight response. They are two separate events, albeit moments apart.

While this separation is not noted in the theories or in the various treatment options, it has been noted by internationally recognised anxiety disorder specialists.

One psychiatrist quotes a patient's description of her panic attacks which begin with 'a tingling feeling going up my spine which enters my head and causes a sensation of faintness and nausea. I feel I'm going to lose control or lose consciousness. I thought I was going to die and started to panic ...' (Hafner 1986).

Another psychiatrist describes the attack as being associated with a 'rushing sensation of a hot flash surging through the body'. People can experience the sensation as 'sometimes associated with a sick feeling and a sensation of fading out from the world'. This faintness is more like a 'whiteout' than a 'blackout' and the head may literally 'feel light'. The fear of this attack is then followed by the fight-or-flight response (Sheehan 1983).

Note the separation between the 'attack' and the feelings of panic in both examples.

Dr Claire Weekes likened the attack to a white-hot flame, starting 'just below the breast bone, passing through the chest, up the spine, into the face, down the arms and even down to the groin and to the tips of the toes' (Weekes 1992). Although Dr Weekes does not separate the 'white hot flame' from the fight-or-flight response, her description is similar to the two examples just given. Nor are there any of the unusual fight-or-flight symptoms in her description.

This separation between the 'attack' and the panic is very important, and holds the key to recovery for so many of us. I teach people who experience these types of attacks to learn to separate their dissociative symptoms and any accompanying 'sensory shocks' from their thoughts and feelings of panic and anxiety about them. I discuss this in Chapter 8.

The effects

The fifth group of symptoms is the effects we feel as a result of our anxiety disorder and in some cases depression. Many of us can experience what appears to be a severe loss of concentration. I say 'appears' because our concentration can be all encompassing and absorbing, we just don't realise it. Our internal 'radar' is usually constantly scanning for signs of the next attack, the next symptom, the next nasty surprise! At the same time, we take our intellectual understanding to its limit by trying to work out what is happening to us and how we can stop it.

When we try to concentrate on whatever it is we are doing, we find it difficult. Unknowingly, we draw our concentration back into ourselves so that we can keep on 'scanning' and then we become more anxious because we feel we can't concentrate!

We may experience sleeping difficulties. We may not be able to sleep; we may sleep fitfully; we can wake up with a nocturnal panic attack; we may wake in the early hours of the morning and not be able to go back to sleep.

We feel the lack of sleep in the heaviness of our head and body. It is as if we are needing to 'drag' ourselves around. And, of course, the more we worry about this, and our sleeping difficulties, the less sleep we will have and the effects continue.

Two of the most distressing effects are what appears to be the loss of feelings towards our partner, children, family and friends. We can also experience a loss of libido. While the loss of libido can be a side effect of antidepressants, people who are not using them also report this effect.

If we look at our overall experience and our various fears, we can begin to see how our loss of feelings occurs. Many of us feel as if we are fighting to survive, fighting to stay sane, fighting not to lose control in some way, or embarrass ourselves in some way. As a result, we simply don't have the energy or 'space' to feel anything else. Obviously, we become anxious over our loss of feelings and this keeps it keeping on!

Sleeping difficulties can leave us feeling exhausted. Some people don't have these difficulties, but they can also feel completely exhausted every waking moment. Again, if we look at our overall experience, we are using so much energy. The fight-or-flight response can be continually activated as we fight our anxiety and panic, sometimes each moment of the day. Is it any wonder we feel so exhausted?

We can also feel physically weak if we are not eating properly. We may be feeling too nauseous or unwell to eat. If we are not eating, or if we are eating very lightly, we will also experience the effects of this. We can feel light-headed, dizzy, shaking, trembling, we may have a headache. We can lose weight. We usually don't recognise these effects for what they are, an effect of not eating, and so we worry about them, and they join the ever expanding panic and anxiety cycle.

In essence, the effects of our anxiety disorder create more anxiety and panic which in turn increases our anxiety, which compounds the effects!

Checklist of symptoms

Use the checklist below to help you understand how your symptoms are being created. Some symptoms can overlap into other groups. For example, the physical response to not eating properly includes feelings of dizziness and of being light-headed. These symptoms can also belong to the hyper-ventilation group as well as the dissociative group.

Not eating properly can make us more vulnerable to dissociation and, if we do dissociate, we may experience additional symptoms of dizziness and light-headedness. We may panic or become anxious about these and then hyperventilate, which can create similar symptoms yet again.

Is it any wonder that we get confused! The more mindful we become, the more we will be able to isolate which of these groups of symptoms we are experiencing. Then we can learn how to turn them off!

If we dissociate, then we need to be aware of how we are inducing these trance states. Are we staring, under fluorescent light, deeply absorbed in our thoughts? We can break the trance state by taking a deep breath, blinking, or by letting go of the absorption in our thoughts. I discuss this in detail in Chapter 8.

Many of our symptoms come from the fight-or-flight response. And we turn these symptoms 'off' by learning to manage our panic and anxiety thinking (see Chapter 8). As we learn to manage our attacks and anxiety, the effects we experience as a result of our disorder dissipate.

Symptom checklist

DISSOCIATIVE SYMPTOMS

- [ ] Derealisation: feeling that you and/or your surroundings are not real; experiencing your surroundings through a diffused light, fog or mist.
- [ ] Depersonalisation: feeling detached from the body.
- [ ] Feeling as if you are floating.
- [ ] Feeling as if your body has expanded.
- [ ] Feeling as if your body has become smaller.
- [ ] Feeling as if you are falling into a void.
- [ ] Tunnel vision.
- [ ] Oversensitivity to sound everyday noise/sound is amplified.
- [ ] Oversensitive to light and colours; an increase in the depth and brightness of colours.
- [ ] Oversensitive to taste.
- [ ] Oversensitive to smell.
- [ ] Oversensitive to touch.
- [ ] Visual distortions; stationary objects appearing to move/sway.
- [ ] Dizziness.
- [ ] Light-headedness.
- [ ] Feeling as if you are going to faint.

SENSATIONS THAT MAY ACCOMPANY DISSOCIATIVE SYMPTOMS

- [ ] 'Electric current' moving through the body.
- [ ] Rush of unusual intense energy through the body.
- [ ] Intense burning heat moving through the body.
- [ ] Burning tingling heat moving through the body.
- [ ] Wave-like motion moving through the body.
- [ ] Hot prickly sensation moving through the body.
- [ ] Ants-crawling sensation moving through the body.
- [ ] Intense cold sensation moving through the body.
- [ ] Intense cold burning heat sensations moving through the body.

FIGHT-OR-FLIGHT RESPONSE

- [ ] Racing heartbeat.
- [ ] Heart palpitations.
- [ ] 'Missed' heartbeats (eptopic).
- [ ] Rapid shallow breathing.
- [ ] Difficulty breathing.
- [ ] Difficulty taking a deep breath.
- [ ] Nausea.
- [ ] Burning/churning in the stomach.
- [ ] Indigestion.
- [ ] Shaking.
- [ ] Trembling.
- [ ] Diarrhoea.
- [ ] Vomiting.
- [ ] Loss of bladder control.
- [ ] Perspiring.
- [ ] Burning red face.

HYPERVENTILATION AS A RESULT OF RAPID SHALLOW BREATHING

- [ ] Pins and needles.
- [ ] Feeling light-headed.
- [ ] Feeling dizzy.
- [ ] Feeling faint.

MUSCLE TENSION AS A RESULT OF FIGHT-OR-FLIGHT RESPONSE

- ☐ Chest pain.
- ☐ Left arm pain.
- ☐ Neckache.
- ☐ Headache.
- ☐ Jaw pain.
- ☐ Leg pain.
- ☐ Choking sensation.
- ☐ Tightening in the throat.

EFFECTS

- ☐ Loss of appetite
  - feeling faint
  - feeling dizzy
  - Feeling lightheaded
  - shaking and trembling
  - feelings of physical weakness
  - weight loss.
- ☐ Loss of concentration.
- ☐ Extreme exhaustion.
- ☐ Loss of feelings towards loved ones.
- ☐ Loss of libido.
- ☐ Sleeping difficulties.
- ☐ Feeling heavy headed.
- ☐ Headache.
- ☐ Feeling dazed.
- ☐ Flu-like symptoms.
- ☐ Sinus problems.
- ☐ Earache.
- ☐ Aching joints.
- ☐ Left-sided weakness.

MAJOR FEARS

- ☐ As if you are having a heart attack.
- ☐ Going to die.
- ☐ Going insane.

- Going to lose control
  - vomiting
  - diarrhoea
  - loss of bladder control
  - literally losing control.
- As if you are going to faint.
- Making a fool of yourself.
- Embarrassing yourself in some way.

From: Angie
SUBJECT: YES!

I was thinking about when I first found this group. I was having a very hard time with panic and anxiety. I have been dealing with the disorder for about five years, having a remission for about two years, and then it came back stronger than ever. I didn't have complete agoraphobia, but I was very anxious going anywhere or doing anything.

I used to have panic attacks that would last for hours, leaving me exhausted and scared out of my mind. I do still get some anxiety, dizziness and dissociation, but I have learnt not to fear these and they pass pretty quickly. I can still have some attacks but I have learnt not to worry about them either. It's wonderful!

CHAPTER 5

SKILFUL COMPASSIONATE ACTION

> **From: Martha**
> **SUBJECT: SECURITY**
> I think if we aren't grounded emotionally, or don't spend time caring for ourselves, we become emotional vampires. We seek approval, love and acceptance from others and if we don't get it, we go berserk frantically trying to conform to what someone else wants. We have never learnt to nurture ourselves when the bad times come. Or else, we spend so much time in denial over the obvious problems in our lives, so that we don't have to confront the truth. Becoming secure inside ourselves is the real cure of this disorder. We need to learn to nurture ourselves, find ways to comfort ourselves and deal with our issues head on, regardless of the outcome.

Martha has made the definitive comment about 'the real cure of this disorder'. But how do we become secure within ourselves? How do we learn to nurture ourselves, find ways to comfort ourselves and deal with the issues head on? The answer is hidden in the following two sentences of her email.

1. 'We seek approval, love, acceptance from others . . . trying to conform to what someone else wants.'
2. 'Becoming secure . . . learning to nurture ourselves, finding ways to comfort ourselves.'

Can you pick the defining aspect in these two sentences?

The first sentence shows how we are not accepting ourselves or being responsible for ourselves. We seek approval and acceptance from other people and conform to what they want or need. And by doing so we betray our responsibility to ourselves.

In the second sentence, learning to become secure within ourselves, caring about our self and taking our issues head on is not only self-acceptance and self-responsibility in action, but overall it is skilful compassion in action.

People will say to me that they will accept themselves once they have recovered. Some people also comment that they may then like themselves enough to be able to care about themselves. It doesn't work like that!

Self-acceptance and self-responsibility are pivotal to the recovery process, and the pivot itself is skilful compassionate action. If we don't accept ourselves, how can we expect our anxiety to disappear? If we are being responsible for other people, and not ourselves, how can we recover? We are not able to, because not accepting ourselves means we are in conflict with ourselves, and this generates much of our underlying anxiety. This is not skilful, nor is not being responsible for ourselves.

Let me clarify how I am using the word 'responsibility'. We are a very responsible group of people. In fact, we are too responsible! Needing to be all things to all people, taking on their problems, being responsible for their happiness, and other feelings means we completely ignore ourselves.

We are perfectionists in everything we do. We go above and beyond the call of duty. A psychiatrist once commented that, if an employer hired five people with an anxiety disorder, they could retrench twenty other staff members, because people with an anxiety disorder do the work of five people without complaint! And we know this is so true!

For most people anxiety disorders are stress-related, and our need to be all things to all people is an enormous and unnecessary stress. In seeking acceptance and approval from others, we suppress our own feelings, our needs and wants. If we add the day-to-day stress of living and the major stresses that come our way, we can see that the development of our anxiety disorder is a natural response to all of the above.

Another way of looking at agoraphobia is to see it as a protection, not so much from panic attacks or panic-like symptoms, but more of a protection from ourselves! If we are confined by the invisible boundaries of agoraphobia, we are limited in what we can do for others. Although agoraphobia can destroy our lives as we knew them to be, at the very least we give ourselves a break from the demands we place upon ourselves.

I speak about our recovery as being the integration of our emotional development with that of our intellectual development. Learning to accept ourselves and learning to become responsible for ourselves is part of this. Learning is the operative word. We can't go from non-acceptance to full acceptance in a minute. We need to learn about ourselves and how to become responsible for ourselves. These are key elements in the recovery process.

From: Angie
SUBJECT: RESCUE

I still have work to do on my recovery, but it is an ongoing process. I know that I will fully recover from this disorder. The most important part for me is taking my time, and not beating myself up because I am not recovering as fast as I would like to. There is a lot of work involved in the process, but it is worth every minute you put into it.

When I first realised that I had to do the work, I was upset because I just wanted something to make it go away so I could get on with my life. But I realised 'no one is coming to rescue me'. That was a big revelation for me. 'I *have* to do this *myself*?? I *can't* do this!!' But you know what, I am doing it and it is great. You learn things about yourself that you would never have believed possible.

How often do we think: 'I can't do this, this is too hard, I am stupid, I'll never get it right, I'll fail'? And with these words we sabotage ourselves even before we start. Yes, it is hard work, but we are not stupid, and when we are being responsible for ourselves we won't fail — we will get it right!

Skilful compassionate action is the life raft, and self-responsibility and self-acceptance are the powers that can take us to full recovery and beyond. Not just to freedom from our disorder, but also to the freedom and security of being ourselves.

Compassion

Take a moment to stop and think. Would you treat other people with an anxiety disorder in the same way as you are treating yourself? Would you treat them with contempt? Dislike? Loathing? Hatred? Would you think, and tell them, they are stupid, weak, a failure or hopeless? Would you tell them they should just pull themselves together and get over it? Of course not. So why are you doing this to yourself? When other people are in pain, we do not abuse them, ignore them, run from them or hide from them. Yet this is what we are doing to ourselves.

Many people with an anxiety disorder will say to me that all they want to do is to help other people who have a disorder. They say they do not want anyone else to experience the degree of suffering they have. Yet they don't recognise that they themselves are in need of the care and attention they so willingly want to give other people. We need to begin to care for ourselves the way we would care for another person with an anxiety disorder. We need to become our own 'rescuer'. And we *can* 'rescue' our self.

Compassion is the non-violation of self and the non-violation of others. In other words, no harm to self or others. *No harm to self.* Many of us don't recognise how much we do harm ourselves. Our mental self-abuse, the lack of kindness, care and respect we show ourselves, causes a great deal of harm. Not only does it generate anxiety and depression, it compounds our already low self-esteem.

Compassion is skilful, active and powerful. This is not how we normally view compassion. In fact, compassion can be a difficult concept to fully understand, especially when we speak about becoming compassionate for ourselves. Many of us feel that this is being selfish, egocentric or perhaps self-pitying. Compassion is none of these. It is our recognition and active response to our pain and suffering.

From: Angie
SUBJECT: COMPASSION
Something came up and I was having some anxiety and I asked myself, if someone in the group had this problem, what would my advice be to them. I followed my own advice and it worked out great. We are all very good at helping other people, but not real good at helping ourselves. Maybe it is the compassion we have for other people. Couldn't we give this compassion to ourselves? Just a thought.

> **From: Karen**
> **SUBJECT: COMPASSION**
> Angie, great thought! I have often said to myself, 'If I put as much effort into loving and caring for myself as I put into loving and caring for others, I'd be so full of self-esteem I'd be bursting.' Also, if I put as much effort into getting me to like me as I put into getting others to like me, there'd be no problem there either!

So why don't we do this? It is healthy! But we can't try to like or love ourselves. This is a mistake many people make. It doesn't work like this. I remember a conversation I had with a client that is a classic example of the way we think about this. He said to me:

Client: I know I have to like myself.
Bronwyn: You *have* to like yourself? Whether you like it or not, you *have* to like yourself? What is the big flaw in your statement?
Client: Have to.
Bronwyn: Yes. *Have* to.
Client: I suppose I should, anyway.
Bronwyn: *Should?*
Client: Okay, okay, no shoulds. But you have read all the books. You know that we have to like ourselves or we have to love ourselves. I tried. I can't. It just makes everything worse.

We have read all the books, stood in front of countless mirrors, telling ourselves that we are special, unique, that there is no one else like us in the universe, and that we love ourselves. The problem with this though is — we *do* feel we are special, we *do* feel we are unique and we *do* feel there is no one else in the universe like us, but we feel this in a disrespectful and disparaging way! Any feelings of love we try to conjure up are lost among the fragments of glass of the countless mirrors we have broken in anger and despair. Trying to like ourselves, love ourselves because we have to, because we should, only increases the contempt we have for ourselves.

If we feel we *have to* care, like or love ourselves, then we are going to be in very big trouble! Because *having to* or *should* means these feelings are not coming naturally. 'I have to' and 'I should' tell us this is another area where we feel we have failed. 'Have to' or 'should' traps us and gives us no choice. We either 'have to' or we fail. There is no middle ground.

We can't manufacture feelings of liking or loving ourselves. They arise naturally, as a result of our caring enough about ourselves to treat ourselves with dignity and respect. Liking and loving ourselves is an *effect* of skilful compassionate action. When we can care for, accept and be responsible for ourselves, we appreciate and feel secure within because we are not betraying or invalidating ourselves.

How do you feel about you?

1. Do you like yourself?
2. Love yourself?
3. Dislike yourself?
4. Loathe yourself?
5. Hate yourself?
6. Feel apathetic towards yourself?
7. Never thought about it?

Do you recognise how points 1 and 2 impact on your mental health?
Do you recognise how points 3 to 7 impact on your mental health?

The first step in learning to care about ourselves is to become open to the idea that we are actually able to! If you were speaking with another person with an anxiety disorder how would you advise them if they:

- thought their mental health was less important than other people's mental health?
- felt selfish in caring about themselves?
- felt guilty in doing so?
- could not accept themselves as they are?
- felt that being responsible for themselves was egocentric or selfish?

How would you:
- comfort them?
- try to ease their pain and suffering?

How can you:
- comfort yourself?
- ease your own pain and suffering?

Self-acceptance

From: Jill

SUBJECT: FEELING A FAILURE

I started off having a really positive day, to now having feelings of failure. I was telling a friend of my latest achievement in working with my panic disorder and she said I shouldn't have done it. I should have worked on other issues, and she asked me why wasn't my therapist working on these issues rather than other ones.

Needless to say I feel like everything I have achieved, and to me it was a lot, was a waste and I haven't achieved anything. I guess I wanted her to be pleased for me and not be negative.

My therapist and I have been working on 'you don't need approval', and that was working well until now. I've felt it very important to discuss my issues with family and friends, but some just seem to let me down.

There are others who have told me they are so pleased with the work I have been doing, so why would someone who says they understand my experience be so hurtful?

Back to the drawing board, I suppose. I guess I will analyse this one for hours on end. Or maybe I shouldn't feel sorry for myself, and maybe just choose a selected few people that understand where I am coming from to talk to.

From: Vicki

SUBJECT: FEELING A FAILURE

There is only one thing that has changed, Jill, you have become aware of your friend's attitude. The important thing to remember is how do *you* feel about your achievement. You need to accept you, including everything you are achieving.

Trust how *you* feel and don't be swayed by other people's opinions. Learn to trust who you tell your innermost thoughts to. You don't need to avoid everyone. Just be aware that things you may hear from other people could be coming from their own needs which they are projecting onto you. Take that into account, and don't take on board unhelpful thoughts and attitudes of other people.

Learning to put ourselves first, and work with the cause of our pain and suffering is skilful compassionate action. It means we are beginning to accept ourselves, and that we are taking responsibility for ourselves. I know some people struggle with self-acceptance because they feel that they have to accept that they are weak, stupid, hopeless and all the other abusive thoughts we can think. But this is not the case. We are none of these things! These are misperceptions on our part. We will only realise this as we work through the process of recovery. There may be aspects of ourselves we want to change, and we can do this once we accept ourselves as we are right now.

Accepting ourselves right now, in this moment, means that we accept our strengths and perceived weaknesses. I say 'perceived' because we do perceive that we are weak, along with everything else! We are not weak, nor is having an anxiety disorder a sign of weakness. We have demanded and expected too much from our self for too long, and now we have been put 'on notice' to take our foot off the brakes and allow our emotional development to unfold.

From: Margaret
SUBJECT: SELF-ACCEPTANCE
Before I started working on this stuff I truly thought my self-esteem was okay, but now I can see that I accept myself on a pretty superficial level and with a heap of conditions attached.

 This bit about acceptance is pretty strong stuff, though. I mean, it's asking a real lot to accept ourselves! I'm working on it though.

When we can accept our self as we are, we accept the reality of ourselves and our circumstances as they are, not how we want them to be, should have to be or must be! We use so much energy trying to think away the reality of our experience and ourselves. 'If only. Once I recover. Once my self-esteem is higher. If this happens I can change. If that happens I can recover.'

We can wish and hope for change. But it is only when we accept ourselves in this current moment that we find we have a direction we can work towards. Instead of asking the question, 'Why am I like this?' we find the answer to it.

The table on the next page highlights the difference between non-acceptance and acceptance.

Non-acceptance	Self-acceptance
Unskilful action	*Skilful action*
• wanting everything to change	• being able to change
• drifting	• having a direction
• avoidance of our strengths	• acceptance of our strengths
• avoidance of our 'weaknesses'	• acceptance of any weakness; choosing to work with it and transform it
• feeling guilty about ourselves	• accepting ourselves as we are without blame
• using energy in avoiding ourselves	• using our energy to change and develop
• a continual sense of unease	• a sense of initiative and intuition
• feelings of being out of control	• feelings of being in control
• being who we think we should be	• being ourselves

Accepting ourselves doesn't mean that we accept 'This is me and I am hopeless! This is my lot in life and I can't change.' It means 'This is me right now as I am at this moment. What can I do to help me become the person I want to be?'

Self-acceptance is something we need to consider and, when we do, we can be open to the possibilities of who we can be and how our life can be. If we accept the challenge, it is a process of learning about and understanding ourselves. The more we learn, the more exciting this becomes, because we begin to realise the potential of who we could be.

From: Vicki

SUBJECT: WHAT IF I'M NOT GOOD ENOUGH

Karen, it is your thoughts! Look at them and also look at why you are persisting with them. Get your therapist to help you with this. You can practise like mad, have all the successes in the world, but if you decide to pick up those 'what ifs' when you come home, rather than say, 'Great, I'm getting there', it will undo the successes every time. This is where you need to work now. I think there is something important in here for you to see.

From: Karen

SUBJECT: WHAT IF I'M NOT GOOD ENOUGH

Vicki, you are absolutely right about this. I do this in every area of my life, not just anxiety and panic. No matter what I do, it's not good enough. 'I'm not good enough' is basically the underlying theme of my thoughts. Back to healthy self-esteem and anxiety cannot coexist, eh? Maybe I'm concentrating too much on the anxiety itself, and not enough on me, my self-worth, belief and trust in myself and my abilities. Maybe I should focus more on breaking this habit of invalidating myself and beating myself up. I think that the answer lies in loving yourself, being com-passionate with yourself and refuting that negative self-talk that really deflates your self-esteem. Thanks Vick.

From: Vicki

SUBJECT: I'M NOT GOOD ENOUGH

You are on track here, Karen, but loving yourself means different things to different people. If you find yourself doing what you perceive as 'unlovable things' this can bring you down. And if you find loving yourself difficult, you may feel a failure at this one too.

Better to adopt the attitude of being kind to yourself. Determine to be your own friend, always there for you no matter what. This is more substantial than the cute rose-coloured glasses thing.

Accepting our disorder

In accepting ourselves as we are, we also accept that we have an anxiety disorder, and there are two aspects of acceptance in this. The first is accepting we do have an anxiety disorder without feeling guilty about it, and without mentally abusing ourselves — 'I'm stupid, weak, hopeless.' This is not skilful or compassionate! These thoughts only generate further anxiety and depression.

When we develop our anxiety disorder it seems as if it is the 'proof' of how weak or stupid we are. This can be particularly so if we have spent years trying to fight our anxiety and panic to no avail. We don't recognise or acknowledge the fact that we may not have been diagnosed for years, and/or we have not been taught any effective management skills. Yet we expect that we should be able to 'pull ourselves together', even when our doctors did not know exactly what it is we are experiencing! We are not weak or stupid and part of our overall recovery is learning to accept the truth of this!

Some people think that, if they accept they have an anxiety disorder, then they will have it for the rest of their life. Other people don't like 'labels' and will reject a diagnosis of an anxiety disorder because of this.

When we accept we have an anxiety disorder, it doesn't mean we will have it for the rest of our life. There is much more chance of this happening if we don't accept it! Once we accept it, we then have a starting point to begin the process of recovery. This also applies to 'labels'. If we reject the 'label' of an anxiety disorder, how do we recover? What is it we are trying to recover from?

Stages of acceptance

From: Martha
SUBJECT: THE CAGE
A real light bulb, 'semi dim', went off in my head. I guess in order for me to get over this, I must simply put myself out there and experience those 'feelings'. But I don't want to feel those sensations, the dizziness, the depersonalisation, the hammering heart, the sweat running down my face, the feeling as though I want to run. Where can I run? I can't run away from myself. No matter how far I run, I still bring myself along.

I guess the true test of how bad I want freedom is how hard I am willing to work for it . I know I want it. But do I want it bad enough to feel the symptoms? Do I want it bad enough to risk having an attack? Or making a fool of myself? Or dying?

These are the kinds of thoughts that go through my head. I haven't had a true panic attack since last summer, probably because I have avoided everything that I thought would give me one. But I am not making any progress, instead I am giving in to those thoughts and they are caging me in. I suppose I've been waiting for some magic 'thing' to come along and take it away. Wishful thinking?

Apparently, the answer lies in my willingness to take a risk, and I have to be honest, I am afraid. In fact, this is the scariest thing I have ever done in my life. Yet I can remember things that I once did that would make this look pale in comparison. I am at a loss for words for my own cowardice.

We are not cowards. Living with an anxiety disorder on a daily basis takes an enormous amount of strength and courage, and we need to recognise and accept this also.

Everyone says to me, 'I just want to recover.' And my answer is, 'How much do you want to recover?' And I say this for a reason, because of course we want to recover, but the full extent and power of our need and desire for recovery is hidden by our fears and symptoms.

We have always been very passive people and we are very passive in our approach to our disorder. We all need to reach the point where 'enough is enough' and we begin to confront our fears, anxiety and panic head on. This is a three-stage process.

FIRST STAGE

The first stage is passive, and during this we all go through a period of complete non-acceptance and outright denial. This can range from a day or so to many months. No matter what we are told, no matter how many doctors we see, no matter how many clinical diagnostic tests we have, we simply don't believe that our symptoms and fears are those of an anxiety disorder.

We try to pull ourselves together and we fight what is happening to us in the only way we know how. We resist it, we tense against it, we fight it mentally — 'I am not like this. How can this be happening to me?' — and the only thing that happens to us is that our anxiety and panic become stronger.

We are confused and frightened. It is during this stage that we can begin to develop agoraphobia. Ultimately, we exhaust ourselves in the fight and begin to accept we have an anxiety disorder, which then generates even more fear. 'This is not me.' And while we accept our disorder at an intellectual level, we are still caught up emotionally in the fear of our attacks and anxiety symptoms.

We 'cage' ourselves in and wait impatiently for the next magic drug to be released, or the next magic cure to come along. We wait for our doctors or therapists to set us free. But this doesn't happen and won't happen. Of course, they give us the support we need, but ultimately it is up to us to open the door of our cage and begin the process of working through to recovery.

SECOND STAGE

Once we accept we do have an anxiety disorder, we move into the second stage which is also passive. We may feel comfortable within a certain radius of our 'safe' places, home or work, but our fears still dominate. We may try to practise a cognitive behavioural program, but if we have an attack or become highly anxious we may run back into our cage and bolt the door! And we still wish and hope for the magic drug or cure.

We can stay at this stage for some time. Then one of two things may happen. Our panic and anxiety can intensify, and we feel ourselves slipping back to our original confusion of complete non-acceptance. Or we become angry and frustrated at our limitations, at the nagging anxiety and the constant fear of having another attack. 'Enough is enough!' Our anger and frustration become stronger than our fears, panic and anxiety and we move into the third and final stage of acceptance. We are no longer passive in our approach to our disorder. We become proactive.

THIRD STAGE

We feel the need to recover in every cell of our being, and we know that nothing is going to stand in our way of it. Our attitude becomes: 'No matter what the cost, I am going to recover' — and I don't mean financial cost! 'No matter what the cost' means that we become disciplined in our approach to recovery. We make time to meditate, or use a progressive muscle relaxation technique. We become disciplined in a mindfulness technique or other cognitive techniques, and we work on our avoidance behaviours. We practise every day and, although we are still overcome by our fears and symptoms, we pick ourselves up and we take them head on again and again. Quoting another email from Martha, we wrestle our disorder to the ground! And we win.

From: Karen

SUBJECT: ACCEPTING

I've been dealing with the morning anxiety by taking Vicki's advice and trying to just accept it. This was very hard for me, because I considered morning anxiety to be a sign that I was not making progress. I also tend to think of it in terms of 'Oh no, it's still here, I'm not getting better, I'll always feel this way . . .' Of course, that only makes the anxiety worse and brings you down.

Before I go to bed I now say out loud, 'Okay, I give myself permission to have morning anxiety. I'm still learning new things and changing and growing, and it's okay to still feel anxious. It's not going to last forever.'

A lot of times I wake up and it's not there! Sometimes it is there, and I find I have to catch myself before I really run with the anxiety and get all upset. When I find the anxiety is there, I say to myself, 'Okay, just some morning anxiety. It doesn't mean anything. I'll just get up and go about my day anyway. It won't be like this forever.' Then I get up immediately and get my day started.

I used to lay there, do some relaxation tapes, wait and watch myself for signs of the anxiety going away, or getting worse. This did *not* work. The more I focused on the feeling, the more I was aware of it. I found the best approach was to just acknowledge it, accept it and get out of bed.

Self-responsibility

Accepting our disorder, and accepting ourselves for developing it, is skilful action and is the first step in recovery. It is also the first of a series of steps we take in becoming responsible for ourselves.

In one particular workshop, I asked participants what self-responsibility meant to them during the recovery process. They answered:

- Recognising that our mental health is just as important as our physical health.
- No one's mental health is more important than our own.
- Working in partnership with our self, not in opposition to our self.
- Treating ourselves with dignity and respect.
- Acknowledging and accepting the fact we have an anxiety disorder. That our doctor would not have made the diagnosis if they were not sure. If we doubt it, then it is our responsibility to seek a second opinion. Once the diagnosis is confirmed, we need to accept it.
- Being totally honest with our doctor about what we are experiencing, including any suicidal thoughts. Our doctor can't make a full assessment of our situation if we are not completely open.
- Recognising that asking for and accepting help is healthy. There is no reason to feel guilty or bad about doing so.

- If our doctor doesn't have current knowledge of anxiety disorders, it is our responsibility to find a doctor who does.
- Becoming informed about any medication we are taking.
- Seeing there is a choice in everything we think and do.
- Making a commitment to ourselves to work through to recovery.
- Taking responsibility for our own recovery from this moment on.
- Taking responsibility for doing whatever we need to do for ourselves.
- Recognising and accepting that working towards recovery is not selfish, but healthy.
- Not blaming ourselves for having an anxiety disorder.
- Accepting the fact that we are not weak, stupid or hopeless.
- Stopping the mental self-abuse.
- Learning all we can about our anxiety disorder.
- Understanding our symptoms and why they are happening.
- Becoming disciplined in practising meditation or another relaxation technique.
- Learning and practising mindfulness or other cognitive skills.
- Becoming disciplined in working to overcome our avoidance behaviour.
- Not worrying about what other people think.
- Not trying to have the perfect recovery.
- Developing the all powerful, all responsible attitude of 'I am going to recover, no matter what!'
- Making our recovery our number one priority.

Using the above list, what points do you need to develop and incorporate into your recovery program?

From: Lorrie
SUBJECT: SELFISHNESS
How on earth does a person sort out whether they are being selfish, and not taking the time to be there enough emotionally for those we love?

From: Karen

SUBJECT: SELFISHNESS

I am going through this a bit myself. I think we are so used to being everything to everybody that when we try to be something to ourselves we feel selfish right away. Actually, I don't think anyone with panic disorder has it in them to be truly selfish, in the negative sense of the word. We're just so darn nice and considerate! LOL. There is nothing wrong with putting your own needs ahead of others, especially during recovery. This doesn't mean you have to tell someone to get lost or take their problems somewhere else, but you can tell them that now is not a good time, can you talk or help tomorrow or in a few days. That is taking care of the self. I think it's one of the more difficult changes to make during recovery, learning to put ourselves first.

P.S. I'd rather be considered selfish, than have panic disorder. Wouldn't you?

THE SENTINEL

My thoughts
are like the crest of waves
on the ocean of consciousness;
Supported and held high by wordless troughs
rolling endlessly toward the beach
And I, as awareness, stand perched upon the hill
For I am the silent sentinel
battle-scarred and weary
The warrior at the beachhead
searching out the darkness,
as the waves roll in.

I stand there, dressed in a hair coat of pain
that irritates my spirit and itches at my soul.
I scratch at bloodied sores until
the ground beneath my feet is soaked,
and all that was solid crumbles away
and I'm cast down onto the shores of mindlessness
Broken on the rocks of dark despair
and the waves roll in.

I lie there
watching seasons come and go
waiting for the tide to change.
Self pity laps at my breast
as I wile away the hours
building sand castles for empty people,
lofty towers with no meaning
and the waves roll in.

Until,
like a tidal wave in the sea of consciousness
comes a thought which washes away illusion
and I'm liberated in body and soul.
The warrior at the beachhead is no more,
the silent sentinel is gone
My thoughts no longer waves upon an ocean
And I, as awareness,
am the ocean.

Carolyn Barker

CHAPTER 6

MEDITATION

Why meditation?

I teach people to meditate for a number of reasons. First, as a relaxation technique and, second, because meditation is the oldest cognitive technique in the world. Its simplicity and gracefulness have stood the test of time.

The cognitive aspect of meditation is different from western cognitive therapies. The major difference is the practice of mindfulness, which is the fundamental principle of meditation. Mindfulness teaches us to detach ourselves from the thinking process. It separates thinker from thought. Mindfulness teaches us to observe and watch the play of the mind. To see how we move from one thought to another, from one mind game to another. As we observe this process, we see very clearly that we do have a choice in what we think about. We can either choose to be a player in the mind games, or we can choose to be the umpire of them.

In Western cognitive therapies, there is no separation between thinker and thought. These therapies use various thinking techniques such as realistic thinking, in which we examine our anxiety and panic thoughts and replace them with more objective thoughts. We remain attached to the thinking process and use thought to 'defeat' thought.

Meditation also differs from progressive relaxation techniques. These focus on relaxing our body, muscle group by muscle group. From my experience, these techniques work for some people but many people experience difficulty with them.

One of the main problems with these techniques is that they focus on the body. They don't take into account the fact that many of us are already doing this. We are very much focused on the body! We monitor our symptoms, we are constantly checking for symptoms, and we are continually tensing up, ready for action should we get even a hint of a symptom.

When we begin using a progressive muscle relaxation technique, we can be going though the motions of tensing and un-tensing. But our mind is still on autopilot, scanning to see what the symptoms are doing or not doing, and scanning to see how we are feeling. 'Am I relaxed yet? Why aren't I relaxed?' Or we can be tensing our already tense muscle, then releasing the tension back to our original tenseness. 'Gosh, that feels better!' I don't think so!

Meditation works in the opposite way. Meditation relaxes our minds and our body relaxes in response to this. Meditation also teaches us to become aware of our automatic thoughts, and our monitoring and checking of symptoms. It teaches us to see that we actually do have a choice in what we think about, and teaches us to control our thoughts including, 'Am I relaxed yet? Why aren't I relaxed?'

In this chapter we look at meditation in a number of ways:

- as a relaxation technique;
- to learn mindfulness skills;
- to learn how not to attach to, or empower, thoughts;

- as an exposure technique to dissociative states, including depersonalisation and derealisation;
- as an exposure technique for letting go of the need to be in control.

In the following chapters we learn how to apply the mindfulness skills in everyday life so that we can become :

- mindful of our panic- and anxiety-producing thoughts;
- aware of the intimate relationship between our thoughts and our symptoms;
- aware of any tendency to dissociate.

This will assist us to:

- see how many of our fears and symptoms are being created by the way we think;
- see that we have a choice in what we think about;
- learn not to attach to, or empower, our thoughts;
- learn how to manage and control our thoughts;
- learn to let go of the need to fight our panic attacks and anxiety;
- learn to let our panic attacks and anxiety happen without resistance;
- be aware of and manage any personal tendency to dissociate.

Reading this list, you may be wondering how all this can be achieved simply by meditating once or twice for twenty minutes a day! But it can, if you are motivated and prepared to become disciplined in the practice of meditation.

From: Melony
SUBJECT: NEW MEMBER
I just wanted to say that I started meditating about four months ago with the tapes. I found it a little hard at first, but I now do it every morning without fail. The change in me has been considerable. My family are noticing that I am more relaxed and in control.

I have now 'trained' my family to be patient and consider me in the mornings when I am doing my meditation. I call them my 'exercises'. As well as being able to relax, it has also really helped me understand the concept of letting my thoughts go during the day.

Motivation

We all want to recover, yet some people will hesitate, delay, or refuse to begin to take the necessary steps to enable them to recover. One of the first reasons we delay is 'time'. We simply don't have the time to work on our recovery, despite the fact that our disorder may be taking all the time we have each day!

When I first began to teach people to meditate I was naive. I would say to people 'meditate twice a day for twenty minutes'. They would look at me and say, 'Are you kidding? I have to do this, I have to do that. And I must do this and should do that.' So I would say, 'Okay, meditate once a day for twenty minutes.' They would look at me again and say, 'Are you kidding. I have to do this and I have to do that and . . .'

Usually everything we have to do, must do, should do, is for everyone else! Our recovery needs to be our number one priority, but in most instances we don't recognise or treat our recovery as a priority. It may be number five, ten or twenty on our list of things to do.

When I ask people with an anxiety disorder what it is they need the most, everyone looks at me questioningly and isn't able to give me a definitive answer. When I ask them about their need to recover, they hesitate for a moment and then acknowledge, 'Yes, of course.' Initially, they don't actually see their recovery in the context of a personal need. They are too busy taking care of the needs of everyone else to realise they have needs of their own.

If we are committed to recovery, then we are going to need to make time for it! This means learning to say 'no' to other people and, as we all know, the word 'no' is not in our vocabulary. Yet this is what we are going to need to do, especially in the early stages of the recovery process. Our mental health demands nothing less. This is skilful compassion in action.

Learning to say 'no' can be very frightening, especially when we are putting our own needs before others. We feel it is one of the worst things in life that we can do. We feel guilty, we feel selfish, we feel we are being bad, uncaring, unsympathetic and everything else in between, even just thinking about saying 'no'.

We need to begin to question our beliefs that tell us our needs are not important, or irrelevant, and that our mental health is less important than other people's. Taking time for ourselves to work on our recovery is being responsible for ourselves. It is not being selfish, nor does it have anything to do with selfishness. Working towards our own health is healthy! Not taking the time we need is abdicating our responsibility to our self. If other people argue the point and accuse us of being selfish then we need to ask ourselves: 'Who is it that is being selfish?'

As Melony said, she 'trained' her family so she could take time out to meditate. While there may be some short-term difficulties in learning to say 'no', the long-term benefits to ourselves and our family far outweigh them.

In short, our motivation and priority needs to be for ourselves and our recovery. And making time to meditate each day is the first step towards recovery.

From: Angie

SUBJECT: WHOSE PROBLEM?

My husband thought I should just 'snap out of it'. About three months ago, we were having yet another discussion about my disorder and he said, 'Other people have gotten over this.' I told him, 'Yes, but they take medication and may not be working on their issues.' I told him that he should just accept me the way I am, and he should get over it.

Just remember that your recovery is the most important thing in your life right now, and try not to be side-lined by what other people say or think about you.

When and where

When I am teaching people to meditate I break every rule in the book. The aim of this meditation is recovery, not Nirvana. Well, perhaps the Nirvana of recovery, but as we are not using meditation for spiritual purposes we can allow ourselves to be more flexible. This flexibility enables people to meditate without needing to go through a checklist of 'shoulds' and 'should nots'. How to sit, where to sit, when to sit and when not to sit. The list of 'shoulds' and 'should nots' only creates further worry and anxiety. Meditation just becomes one more thing we have to do. And do perfectly.

The first rule I break is 'when to meditate'. We can meditate any time during the day or early evening. All we need is twenty minutes. This can be in the bus or train on our way to or from work, or during a lunch break, or we can wake twenty minutes earlier in the morning and use this time while family members are still asleep.

We may be able to meditate sometime in the afternoon one day, and find we can schedule a meditation session the following day in the evening. As long as we make a commitment and become disciplined in setting time aside, even if it is only one twenty-minute session a day, we will feel the benefits. And this is all that matters.

The second rule I break is 'do not lie down'. If you feel more comfortable lying down, then do so. Be mindful that lying down does make it easier to go to sleep. And this is the third rule I break, 'do not go to sleep'. Many people are exhausted through their disorder. As they begin to relax, whether they are sitting or lying down, they may go to sleep in the first few weeks of practice. If they do, *so what!* When people go to sleep during meditation, it means they need it! People will stay awake once they are not so exhausted. It also means they have let go of their need to be in control at all times. Learning to let go of this control is one of the most important aspects in recovery.

One rule I do set is 'don't meditate just before going to sleep at night'. As we become more comfortable with meditation, we will find that we can feel revitalised after a session and may not feel like going to sleep. To avoid this happening, schedule any evening meditation session two or three hours before going to bed.

But in contradiction to this, many people have difficulties going to sleep at night as a result of their anxiety. If this is the case, then we can use our meditation technique to put ourselves to sleep at night. When we are ready to go to sleep, we can begin to meditate and allow our self to let go, and our meditation will take us gently and easily into sleep.

In short, we can meditate any time of the day as long as we commit to meditating at least once a day.

Do not disturb!

A number of people say to me that family members don't take them seriously when they ask not to be disturbed while they meditate. Our recovery is most important, as I've said. Our need for privacy and quiet time needs to be respected. Not only will we benefit, so will our family as we begin to recover. Melony asked her family to be patient and to consider her, which they did. As Angie says, 'Don't be side-lined.' Respect your needs, take them seriously, and your family will learn to accept them.

- *Divert the phone.* There is one thing we can be sure of, the phone will not ring all day, but the minute we sit for meditation the 'whole world' will be ringing us!
- *Put the pets outside.* Nothing destroys a meditation session so completely as a cat or dog jumping onto our lap, while we are deep in meditation!

Timing the meditation session

We can meditate either with music or without it. If we prefer to use music, choose a piece of music that will last for twenty minutes.

If we decide to meditate without it, we can use a watch or non-ticking clock to time our session. During our meditation we can gently open our eyes and check the time. If the twenty minutes is not over, we simply return to our meditation. Within a few days we will know when twenty minutes are over without needing to open our eyes.

When our mediation is over, sit quietly for a few minutes. This allows us to come out of meditation gently and quietly.

Don't use an alarm clock or any other timer. Meditation is for relaxing, and we won't be feeling very relaxed if we are brought out of meditation by the ringing or beeping of a clock.

Meditation as a release

When people first learn to meditate, I suggest they only meditate for twenty minutes at a time. Meditation is a 'releasing process'. On occasion we could experience feelings that we have been suppressing, such as our anger or sadness. This is similar to the 'releasing process' that occurs when some people have a massage. They find they feel sad or angry during or straight after the massage. The releasing process doesn't usually begin within the twenty-minute period of meditation. This is the reason I suggest people stay within this time frame. As we become more familiar and comfortable with the actual process of meditation then we can extend our meditation time if we want to, and many people do!

The release of these feelings is healthy and we do need to express them. When we keep them suppressed, they can add extra fuel to our anxiety disorder. I discuss this further in Chapter 11.

From: Jill
SUBJECT: GETTING THERE
I feel like I am beginning to see some light. I have found meditation amazing. I can think a million thoughts while I am there, but I can let them go. I am now putting this into practice during the day. Mind you, I am exhausted. LOL. I am even surprising myself with the way I am aware of what I think, and I can sometimes just let the negative thoughts go!

The mindfulness of meditation

One of the most common problems people have when they first learn to meditate is that they try to think of 'nothing' or to 'blank' their mind. This is a contradiction. The more we try to think of 'nothing' or try to 'blank' our mind, the more thoughts we will have, because these are just thoughts also. 'I have to think of nothing, why can't I think of nothing? Why can't I blank my mind out, blank out, blank out, why can't I do this?'

Meditation is not a process of trying to eliminate all thoughts and feelings. Rather it is a process of letting go of our attachment to our thoughts and feelings. When we can let go of our thoughts, the profound quiet of meditation unfolds gently and naturally.

'Let go of our attachment'? What did you think when you read the word 'attachment'? Did you think, 'What is she talking about?' Did you analyse the word 'attachment', trying to work out exactly what I meant? If so, you became attached to the thought about 'attachment'. You were thinking about what the word meant in this context. And we do become 'attached' to our thoughts every waking moment. A thought rises into consciousness, we attach to it, and we attach to the next thought, and the next, and so on.

How did you feel when you were trying to work out what I meant by the word 'attachment'? Did you feel confused? What many of us don't realise is that our thoughts create our feeling states, including our fears, anxiety, panic and confusion!

Meditation is a process of observing our thoughts rather than attaching to them. We become mindful, we become aware of our thoughts as they rise into consciousness. We see how we attach to our thoughts and become involved with our thinking. In meditation, we let go of our thinking and the thought falls away, and another will rise and fall away, if we don't attach to it. As our meditation deepens, our thoughts slow down and disappear by themselves, as we enter the full meditative state. And in this state there are no thoughts or feelings, only an all encompassing silence and peace.

Meditation techniques

I am going to describe three different meditation techniques that I teach in my workshops. One is a 'word' technique, the second a 'breathing' technique and the third an 'image' technique. These techniques give us an object to focus our mind on. It isn't a matter of analysing the word or becoming involved in the breathing process or creating an elaborate image. They are simply objects that we use to detach from our thoughts.

Our thoughts have always had control over us. Meditation teaches us how to control them. One of my meditation teachers used the analogy that meditation trains our minds in a similar way to how we train a puppy to 'sit' on command. We say 'sit' and the puppy looks at us, 'yeah sure', and runs away. We bring the puppy back and say 'sit'; and it runs away. We bring the puppy back, 'sit', and away it runs again. In time, the puppy learns to 'sit' and in time so will our minds!

We 'sit' our mind on the word, or breath or image and immediately our mind runs away with a thought. We become aware, let the thought go, and bring our mind back and 'sit' it on the word or breath or image; and it runs away again.

This is the process of meditation. Our thoughts are part of this process. Many people think they should not be thinking, and become frustrated when their thoughts constantly break through their mediation. Becoming frustrated means we are attaching to our thoughts about our thoughts!

WORD TECHNIQUE

This technique involves the silent repetition of a word or mantra. The word or mantra becomes the object of our meditation, a point to focus our mind on.

While we can use any word we like, it is preferable to use a short word with one or two syllables. Herbert Benson, in his book *The Relaxation Response*, suggests the word 'one' (Benson 1975).

I always advise people not to use words like 'peace' or 'calm' as these words can have negative associations, such as 'calm down', 'why can't I get any peace'. This is not very conducive to meditation. Some people use a word that has meaning for them, perhaps a word from the Bible. Other people use everyday words such as 'rose'.

Some people prefer a mantra. 'Om', pronounced 'aum', is a well-known mantra. 'Shantih' is another, which has been translated as meaning peace; another mantra is 'sharma', interpreted as meaning quietude.

BREATHING TECHNIQUE

The object of this technique is to focus on our breath. Some people have fears and anxiety associated with their breathing. I advise people who have these particular fears to use either a word or an image technique instead. There are two variations with the breath technique. Both techniques follow the natural rhythm of the breath. There is no need to alter our breathing in any way.

The first technique is to become mindful of the sensation of our breath as we inhale and exhale. Being aware of the sensations of each breath becomes the object of our meditation.

A variation of this is to count each breath. The first breath we take when sitting for meditation becomes breath number one. The next one, 'two', and so on until breath number five. After this breath we begin the count again at 'one', and so on.

IMAGE TECHNIQUE

Some people are more 'visual' and they prefer to visualise an image as their object of meditation. It is important we only use this technique if we are a 'visual' person, otherwise we will have difficulty trying to visualise and we will become frustrated and annoyed — the opposite to what we could be feeling.

If we decide to use this technique, I always advise people to keep the image simple. Some people may visualise a flower or a bird in flight. If we construct a more elaborate visualisation we may spend the whole twenty minutes trying to get it perfect! The more complicated the image we use, the more it keeps us attached to our thoughts!

Practice of meditation

The encompassing framework of meditation is mindfulness. Being aware.

Depending on our individual choice, when we sit for meditation we will:

- silently repeat a word or mantra to ourselves; or
- become aware of the sensations of our breath as we inhale and exhale; or
- focus on the image we have chosen to visualise.

As we do this, our thoughts will break through almost immediately, and we will attach to our thoughts and become involved with them. We need to become aware that we are thinking and not focusing on our object of meditation. We become mindful, we observe, we witness that we are thinking. We let the thought go, and bring our mind back to the word or breath or image. Another thought will rise and we will attach to this one. We become aware that we are thinking, we let go of the thought, and bring our mind back to the object of our meditation.

In summary, when we sit for meditation we:

- focus on the word or breath or image we have chosen;
- lose the focus by becoming attached to our thoughts;
- become aware we are thinking, not meditating;
- let go of our thoughts, stop thinking of them;
- bring our focus back to the object of our meditation;
- become caught up in our thinking again;
- become aware we are thinking, not meditating;
- let go of our thoughts;
- bring our focus back to the object;
- and we will become attached to our thoughts;
- and we let go of our thoughts and we . . .

This is the process of meditation. Some people become annoyed or frustrated as their thoughts break through time and time again. If we are becoming frustrated, be aware that this is also just a thought. Let the thought go and come back to the word, breath or image.

Becoming relaxed

One of the most common problems people have when they are learning to meditate is that they try to relax. We become relaxed when we don't try. As our meditation progresses, we will begin to relax without effort. As we do so, our thoughts will slow down by themselves.

If we are using a word or mantra, we will become aware that our normal inner 'speaking' voice has also slowed down. The repetition of the word or mantra will be slow and possibly drawn out. Let this happen. If we bring our inner repetition back to our normal rhythm, we will bring ourselves out of meditation.

Irrespective of what object we are using in our meditation, our breathing will slow down naturally and easily by itself. Allow the breath to slow down. If we bring the breath back to its normal flow, we will bring ourselves out of meditation.

This also applies to the image we may be visualising. We will lose the clarity of the image. Allow this to happen. If we bring it back into clarity, we will come out of meditation.

Go with whatever happens. These are the signs that we are becoming relaxed. We may reach the point where the object of our meditation and our thoughts disappears completely, leaving us in the all encompassing awareness of the silence of our mind. As Carolyn says in her poem: 'My thoughts no longer waves upon an ocean. And I, as awareness, am the ocean.'

At the end of the twenty minutes, give yourself time to return to your normal waking state. Sit quietly for a few minutes and open your eyes when you feel comfortable.

Meditation is so hard to do because it is so simple!

Don't complicate it by thinking:

- Am I doing this right?
- It has to work, if not I won't recover.
- How do I know if this is right?
- How is this going to help?

- I don't get the point of all of this.
- I should be doing something else.
- Is it happening yet?
- Why can't I just watch television?
- This isn't working. I'll try the breath.
- That doesn't work.
- What about a mantra?
- What does the mantra really mean?
- Is it happening yet?
- I can't do this. I'm useless.
- What will I visualise?
- What's for dinner?
- Maybe I should use the word *and* the breath.
- Am I focusing on the word, breath or both?
- Is it happening yet?
- What am I supposed to feel like?
- Fifteen minutes to go!
- This isn't working.
- I suppose I should try a bit harder.
- I feel a bit silly doing this.
- I don't really have the time.
- What is it supposed to feel like?
- What's for lunch?
- I'm bored.
- I should try the word again.
- Do I really want to use a mantra?
- I will use another word — 'rose'.
- Why isn't it happening?
- I will try and visualise.
- How do I do that?
- Everyone else can do this but me.
- Now I'm confused.
- How do I do that?
- Why isn't it happening?
- Is it twenty minutes yet?
- What am I going to do after this?
- I should try it some other time.
- I can't see how this will work.

These are all just thoughts. Detach from them, let them go and bring your mind back to the object of your meditation!

If meditation is so simple, why is it so hard?

People have many questions when they first begin to meditate. The following is a list of every question I have ever been asked about meditation. Use this list to help you understand any difficulties you may have in regards to your meditation practice. Check the boxes of the points you may be having difficulty with and work your way through them, one by one if you need to, during your meditation session.

☐ Do I have to use music?
Some people prefer to use music, others don't. It is an individual choice.

☐ I feel very self-conscious when I start to meditate.
People can feel self-conscious when they first begin. Be mindful that this is also just a thought. Let it go and bring your mind back to the object of your meditation.

☐ I can't make up my mind whether to use a word or breath or an image.
Some people do become confused. They can spend many sessions trying one or the other, or all three, wondering why they can't meditate. We need to choose one and give ourselves time to become familiar with it. Listen to your intuition. Which one feels more comfortable, more right, for you?

☐ I am not sure about awareness. How do I do that?
Awareness, mindfulness, is 'stepping back' and just watching the passing parade of your thoughts. Instead of attaching to your thoughts, being caught up in them, you detach from them and simply observe, witness them. In one way it is like listening to a talkback radio station with the call sign 'WHO triple one ME'!

☐ I am not sure about letting the thoughts go.
It is a matter of letting them come into your mind and not attaching to them. As you become aware that you are thinking, you can choose not to think them. Let the thoughts go, stop thinking and bring your mind back to the object of your meditation. In much the same way as police direct traffic, we become our own 'thought' police. We can either allow a thought to 'go through', or we can mentally hold our hand in the stop position and 'wave' our attention back onto the object of our meditation.

☐ I seem to have both object and thoughts at the same time.
This can be so for some people. You focus on the word or breath or image, and there is a 'background' of thoughts running through your mind. You attach to your thoughts and they come into the 'foreground' while the object of meditation moves into the background. When you become aware that your primary focus is on your thoughts, let them go and return your focus back to the object. This will bring the object back to the foreground and your thoughts will move to the back.

☐ I don't like seeing my thoughts.

This is only a thought! But, yes, some people are frightened of seeing their thoughts. They think to themselves 'I don't want to know!' and they will avoid meditation and mindfulness. The problem is, we may avoid seeing them but that doesn't mean they disappear! They are still there and they are creating our anxiety and panic, which none of us likes at all! To recover we need to understand our disorder intimately. We need to see the 'nuts and bolts' of it so we can dismantle it.

When you practise mindfulness, you are separating your self from your thoughts. You may not like them, you may be frightened of them at first, but see them for what they are. Thoughts. That's all. They are not the sum total of you. If they were, you would not be able to learn how to control them. And you *can* control them. Just note the thought, 'I don't like seeing my thoughts' and let it go. If you are feeling anxious about them, make a mental note, 'feeling anxious', let go of the thought and let the anxiety be there. Experiment with your thoughts. Learn to see the 'ground rules of the various mind games'. This way, you can be the umpire of the games, rather than a player!

☐ I am scared of how my body feels when I am meditating.

Many people have not been able to relax for so long, they can become frightened of the sensations of their body relaxing. Don't attach to the fearful thoughts. Just note, 'body relaxing', and let the thought go. Let your body feel whatever it is feeling. Just let it happen. The unknowns of meditation become the known with practice!

☐ I can't stop thinking.
☐ I can't blank my mind.
☐ I can't think of nothing.

Don't even try! Trying to stop thinking, trying to blank your mind, trying to think of nothing are simply thoughts. Let them go and come back to the object of your meditation. Your thoughts will slow down or stop completely as you move into the deeper stages of meditation.

☐ My eyes keep wanting to partially open.

Let this happen. Don't fight it. Go with whatever happens.

☐ I am not sure if I am meditating.

☐ Why isn't my meditation happening?

☐ I don't know if I am doing it right.

If you are looking for meditation to happen, then it is almost guaranteed not to! Don't watch and check for signs that you are actually meditating. Let go of your thoughts about it. Meditation happens when we least expect it to.

If you realise your breathing has slowed down, or if the meditation session passed quickly, or if you experienced one or some of the effects listed below, then you were meditating.

☐ My thoughts race out of control.

Simply note 'my thoughts are racing' and bring your mind back to the word, breath or image. They will slow down once you stop giving them the attention.

☐ I am worried about my breathing slowing down.

The slowing down in breathing is a sign your meditation is going well. Note the thought, 'worried about my breathing', and let it go, and come back to the focus of your meditation. Don't attach to the thought, let it fall away. Let whatever happens, happen! Go with the flow of your meditation. If you need to take a deep breath or your breathing needs to return to its normal rate, it will do so automatically.

☐ I get bored.

Note the thought, 'bored', let it go and return to the object of your meditation. Are you sure, though, that your boredom is not part of a need to be in control? A defence against letting go of control? See the 'Need to be in Control' below.

☐ I get distracted by outside noises.

This happens to everyone. I remember once teaching a large group of people to meditate during a winter storm. As we began, a huge thunderstorm moved overhead. The lighting was flashing and the thunder was extremely loud. Then it began to rain very heavily. I thought to myself, no one is going to be able to meditate in this. Yet almost all the group did. They simply noted the noise of the storm, and returned their attention back to the object of their meditation. Simply note your thoughts about being distracted, let them go and come back to the word, breath or image.

☐ All my meditations are different.

And they will be. Some will be great, others won't. Take it as it comes. Each meditation session will teach you more about the overall process, even the ones you think are not so good.

☐ My meditation goes so fast.

You are meditating well! This is what happens when you do.

☐ My meditation goes too slowly.

Are you becoming attached to the thoughts 'When is the time up?' 'How much longer do I have to do this?' Simply note the thoughts, let them go and come back to the focus of your meditation. But be mindful this may be a defence against letting go of control (see below).

☐ I come out of meditation too easily.

This may be happening for a couple of reasons. As your breath slows, you may be bringing your breath back to its normal rhythm. The same for the repetition of the word or mantra. As this slows down, you may be bringing it back to your normal rhythm of your inner speaking voice. If you are using an image and it becomes distorted during meditation, you may be bringing the image back to full clarity. Any of these will bring you out of meditation very quickly. Go with the slowing down of the breath and/or the word or mantra or any distortions of the image. Let it happen.

Or you may be 'on guard', waiting and watching for something to happen and I don't mean waiting for your meditation to happen! You may have your radar turned on checking for symptoms, and/or you may be having difficulty letting go of control (see below).

Or sometimes we may come out of meditation spontaneously, and feel quite refreshed. If this happens, then finish your meditation session and don't attach to your thoughts about why this happened. This is just part of the overall experience of meditation.

☐ I am frightened I will not be able to come out of meditation.

This doesn't happen. Breaking our meditation is easy (see the above question).

☐ I can't seem to make the time to meditate or practise any form of relaxation. This can be more avoidance, rather than not finding the time. Is it perhaps a fear of letting go of control? Or is it because you feel safe within your comfort zone, and feel frightened of doing something new? If so, what can you do to assist you in working through this?

Do you perhaps feel annoyed or frustrated that you 'have' to do something? Many of us think, 'Why do I have to do this?' This comes down to accepting that we do have an anxiety disorder and that much of our recovery is dependent on us.

People do feel resentful about needing to work through their recovery. Although they realise it's unrealistic, there can be the frustration of knowing they have assisted many other people at various times in their life, but when they need assistance no one is there to help them. What can you do to help yourself break this impasse?

☐ I only feel relaxed in meditation. I don't feel relaxed during the day.
This is normal when we first begin to meditate. Keep practising and you will find the benefits will gradually extend into everyday life. Perhaps for only a few minutes in the beginning, but with continued practice you will feel it extending further.

The need to be in control

From: Margaret
SUBJECT: WHO WOULD HAVE THOUGHT!
The other day when I was meditating I had a big rush of anxiety. I usually find meditation quite relaxing. Anyway, instead of fighting it with 'Oh no' thoughts, I decided to practise just letting it happen. Surprise, surprise, my anxiety subsided straight away. I must say it wasn't what I was expecting!

• I want to meditate but can't.
• I am too frightened to meditate.
• I can't let go of control.

- I can't meditate alone.
- I feel very anxious before and when I meditate.
- I feel very tense as I start to meditate.
- I can't sit still.
- I feel frightened after my meditations.

All these observations reflect one need — the need to be in control. We have always needed to be in control of ourselves and our environment. This need to be in control is the 'superglue' that holds in place the many different masks we wear, to enable us to be 'all things to all people'.

The only thing we are not in control of is our thinking. Recovery means that we need to let go of our need to be in control, and learn to control our thinking instead.

Some people can be very frightened of letting go of the control, because they fear their worst fears will come true. They don't. The need to be in control is helping to perpetuate our disorder. We will only recover once we can let go of this control. When we do, the only thing that will happen to us is that we will recover!

It is all right to feel anxious, tense and nervous when we begin to meditate. We are learning a new skill and this new skill is going to take us out of our 'comfort zone'. We need to allow ourselves to feel anxious, to feel tense, to feel frightened. We can 'hold' hands with our fears and anxiety and begin to meditate. Simply let the feelings be there, and don't become attached to the thoughts about them. Let them happen and gently bring the mind back to the object of meditation.

If it becomes too uncomfortable, then we need to be able simply to note 'very uncomfortable' and bring our mind back to the object of our meditation. If we attach to our thoughts about how frightened we may feel, how anxious we may feel, we will only increase these feelings. Let them happen and don't attach to thoughts about them.

If we find we are not able to do this, then finish the meditation session. Not with thoughts of failure or 'I will never be able to do this', but with thoughts of 'I will see how I go tomorrow'.

Even if it means sitting for meditation only for five minutes, this is a starting point. The next day we can see if we can increase this time to six minutes. The following day seven minutes, and so on. The most important point is to practise letting go to the point where we feel comfortable, and then seeing if we can slowly increase it, minute by minute.

Letting go of the need to be in control when we sit for meditation is exactly the same as when we go to sleep at night. Most people don't think about letting go of control when they go to sleep. They simply do it. And nothing happens to them except they go to sleep! Same too with our meditation practice. Nothing happens to us. We simply meditate!

We may be able to meditate and let go of the control without even thinking about it. When we have finished meditating, we may realise that we were indeed meditating and we have actually let go of the control.

Some people can become frightened of this. But this too is just a thought. The fact that nothing happened to them during their meditation demonstrates very clearly that the only thing that does happen is that we relax. Instead of attaching to this fear, we need to attach to the fact that nothing happened to us and nothing will happen to us when we let go of this control.

Effects of meditation

From: Martha

SUBJECT: IS THIS NORMAL?

Can you tell me if the experiences I have been feeling in meditation are normal. My mind does tend to wander in many directions as I repeat my word. But sometimes I feel like my body is floating and I even feel like the bed is moving or else my body is or something. Does this sound weird?

I also find that my breathing is really slow. It is so relaxed and slow, it sort of scares me. I find my thoughts drifting into the fear of perhaps I'll stop breathing, which is totally ridiculous I know. I also worry that I have been meditating while lying down, and today I even fell asleep afterwards.

☐ I see colours swirling when I meditate.
☐ I feel very light.
☐ I feel very heavy.

☐ My thoughts seem to disappear and it is as if I am watching a movie.

☐ I can see images when I meditate.

☐ I feel as if I am floating.

☐ I am losing awareness of my body or parts of my body.

☐ I see a white light or flashes of white light or thousands of pinpricks of white light.

Quite a number of people who dissociate will experience some of these sensations as they are going to sleep at night. And, whether they dissociate or not, people can experience these when they meditate.

As I have said, meditation can become an exposure technique for people who do dissociate. During meditation we can become aware of how easy it is to move in and out of different states of consciousness. We can also realise how peaceful these states can actually be when we don't fear them.

These sensations are also signs that we are relaxing deeply and that our meditation is going well. Let go of any thought associated to them and let them happen. Enjoy!

☐ I can't get used to the sensations. I don't like them.

If we find we are becoming frightened of these sensations, all we need to do is note the thought and turn our mind back to the object of meditation. Don't attach to your thoughts about them, including the thought, 'I don't like them!' Just be aware of the sensations, let them happen and bring your mind back to your object of focus. You will find that you can enjoy these sensations once you let go of any fearful or 'judging' thoughts about them.

☐ I never get these sensations.

Some people will have one or more of these sensations while other people will never have any of them. Nor does it matter if they don't happen. It doesn't mean we are not meditating, it simply means they don't happen. They are simply effects some people can have when they meditate.

'Handy hint' number 403. Don't spend your meditation sessions watching and waiting for any of them to happen. This is guaranteed to ensure they won't.

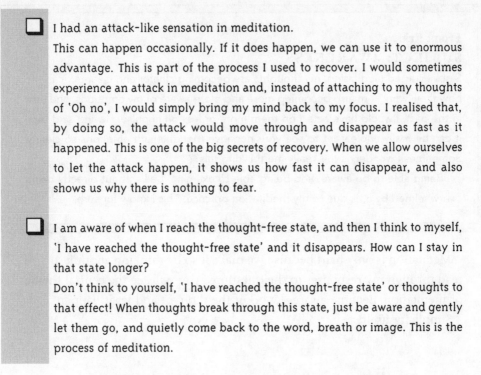

I had an attack-like sensation in meditation.

This can happen occasionally. If it does happen, we can use it to enormous advantage. This is part of the process I used to recover. I would sometimes experience an attack in meditation and, instead of attaching to my thoughts of 'Oh no', I would simply bring my mind back to my focus. I realised that, by doing so, the attack would move through and disappear as fast as it happened. This is one of the big secrets of recovery. When we allow ourselves to let the attack happen, it shows us how fast it can disappear, and also shows us why there is nothing to fear.

I am aware of when I reach the thought-free state, and then I think to myself, 'I have reached the thought-free state' and it disappears. How can I stay in that state longer?

Don't think to yourself, 'I have reached the thought-free state' or thoughts to that effect! When thoughts break through this state, just be aware and gently let them go, and quietly come back to the word, breath or image. This is the process of meditation.

Is the glass half-empty or half-full?

After teaching people to meditate in the workshops, I ask them if they felt their meditation session was beneficial. I also ask what difficulties they may have experienced. It's interesting to note that some people who indicate they had difficulties with their meditation actually didn't! In speaking with them, I find that they may have been anxious as they began to meditate. Or they may initially have had difficulty in letting go of their thoughts, or the need to be in control. Yet overall they felt very relaxed, their breathing had slowed down and the session time had gone quickly.

They were discounting the fact that they were able to meditate successfully. Their mind picked up on the initial difficulties they experienced, and they attached to their thoughts that the session didn't go well. These thoughts are part of the mind games our thoughts play. 'I didn't meditate well, I can't do this, why can't I control my thoughts?' These thoughts are part of the bigger game: 'You're no good', 'You can't do anything right'. And we all become involved with this game!

From: Eric
SUBJECT: AWARENESS

Since I started meditating, my thoughts are becoming clearer and clearer. I can see how they 'work'. I'm also becoming more and more aware of my emotions, and how in the past, I would have acted on them more or less on impulse. Having said that, it can be really unpleasant to see your negative thoughts and emotions so clearly. Sometimes I wonder, is this really me thinking this??

Being able to be aware, and being able to examine it all without directly being overwhelmed by it, is due to my meditation practice. This I know for sure.

Meditation is only hard because we make it so by thinking about it. If you read through my responses to the questions, you will see the central theme of meditation. Become aware, let go of the thought and let it happen!

Simplicity itself!

CHAPTER 7

MIND GAMES

From: Karen

SUBJECT: LIGHT BULB MOMENT

Today a light bulb went off. I've been trying to change the fact that I'm experiencing some physical symptoms, such as morning anxiety, tightness in the throat, heaviness in the chest. I am working with my thoughts, which help these feelings not to escalate, but I think I'm still watching for them to go away. I still get upset when I feel these things, and the thought that I'll never recover soon follows.

Suddenly I realised that I'm not supposed to try to stop these symptoms. I'm supposed to change my perception towards them, towards anxiety in general, and that's when the pressure is taken off. That's when healing can really start.

Is this one of the main keys to recovery? Not just working with our thoughts and our self-esteem, but a complete change in attitude towards our physical symptoms? If so, am I right in saying that this change, from 'what if' to 'so what', is a resolution to live with these sensations a little while longer until our thought work kicks in? That this promotes recovery? In other words, I will still be working on my thinking, but I can change my perception and the rest will take care of itself?

Imagine you have been out bush-walking and you are on your way back to your car. You're feeling hot and tired and it is a relief to see the car in the distance. As you walk towards it, you suddenly realise that a snake lies coiled on the path ahead of you. The snake is between you and your car. You stop and look for a way around the snake. There isn't one, just dense bush on either side of the walking track. You have no doubt that other snakes would be in the undergrowth. You wait for a while, hoping that someone else will come and help you, but no one does.

You begin to walk towards the snake, with slow measured steps. Your heart is pounding as you get closer to it. It doesn't move. You look around for a detour from the path, but again you can't find one. You are surrounded by dense bush to the left and right of you. You stop again. The snake doesn't move.

You creep closer and closer to it. On which side should you pass the snake? If it hears you and takes flight, which way will it go? To the left or to the right? What if it went straight ahead, down the path towards your car? What if it hears you and strikes out of fear? What can you do?

Your heart is pounding so hard you are sure the snake will hear it. Your breathing is fast and shallow. You are perspiring, not from the heat of the sun but as a result of your fear.

You have almost reached the snake. Your whole body is responding to the threat. You stop again, take a deep breath and hold it. You wait for the snake to move. It doesn't. You take another step and the snake still doesn't move. You are now almost beside the snake. You look at it closely and you realise it is simply a piece of rope someone has dropped on the path.

How many times have we done something like this? Not so much with snakes and pieces of rope! But there would have been occasions when you saw something and it turned out not to be what you first thought it was. When driving on a hot day, it appears as if there is water on the road but it turns out to be a mirage. It is just the heat shimmering on the hot surface.

What about the three-dimensional pictures that everyone had a few years ago? Some of us could look at the images and pick up the 'hidden' picture behind it almost straightaway. Other people had to take a closer look before the picture became obvious.

And so too with our attacks and our anxiety. We are perceiving our attacks and anxiety as something other than what they are. We perceive our symptoms as being life-threatening or a threat to our sanity, or a sign that we are about to lose control in some way. While our symptoms can feel very violent, they are not signs of anything other than what they are, symptoms of our attacks, panic and anxiety. They are not what we perceive them to be. This is what we are 'supposed' to feel when we dissociate or have an attack or feel anxious or panic.

It is our fear of our symptoms that is the driving force of our disorder. Lose the fear and we 'lose' the disorder, with its many secondary fears and associated anxiety. This does not necessarily mean we will never dissociate or never have an attack or be anxious again. But once we lose our fear we simply don't care if we dissociate or have an attack occasionally. 'So what!' We know them for what they are. A trance state, an attack. Nothing more. If we feel anxious, 'So what is the anxiety telling us?' Because the more mindful we become, the more we will see that our anxiety will always be telling us something.

Recovery is a change of perception. It is not just changing the way we think about our attacks and anxiety, it is changing the way we see them, the way we perceive them to be. When we can see them as they are, and for what they are, our thinking changes accordingly and we lose our fear of them.

As I said in the opening chapter, we need to bring our emotional development to the level of our intellectual development. Intellectually, many of us know that our attacks and anxiety will not hurt us. We see them for what they are, but we are still trapped in the disorder because, at an emotional level, we do not believe they won't hurt us.

Working with a mindfulness technique enables us to see, at an emotional level, why there is nothing to fear from our attacks or anxiety. And this is the power — to see it and to understand why there is nothing to fear. This is why so many of us can now say 'so what' if we have an attack or if we become anxious. *So what!*

Before we begin to work with a mindfulness technique, it is difficult to grasp the significance of 'so what' because we are caught in the horror of our experience. 'So what' is the acknowledgment and recognition that our attacks and anxiety are simply that. An attack or anxiety. Nothing more. When we are caught up in our disorder, we are not seeing the reality of them. Our fears that are associated with them mean we are not accepting the reality of our experience.

We think we are going to die, go insane, lose control. The reality is, nothing happens to us as a result of our attacks and anxiety. Our worst fears do not come true. When I say this in workshops, I can tell by the expression on everyone's face that they don't believe me. Everyone is thinking to themselves, 'It is going to be me. I am going to be the one who will die from it, go insane from it, lose control in some way.' Why?

As I always say, 'Why will you be the first one this is going to happen to?

Why will you be the first one to be written about as being "The one it happened to"?' Our thought that 'I will be the one' is just another thought. But we give our thoughts the power to destroy our lives.

It is the way we are perceiving and thinking about our experience which disables us and creates havoc in our lives. It is not our attacks or our anxiety as such. It is our fear of them.

The way we think turns on the fight-or-flight response and our symptoms of panic and anxiety are the result. Or we may dissociate and then become caught up in thoughts, which turns on the fight-or-flight response, which again creates our anxiety and panic.

Thoughts → fight-or-flight response → panic and anxiety symptoms
Dissociation → thoughts → fight-or-flight response → panic and anxiety symptoms

> **From: Martha**
> **SUBJECT: THE BIG ONE**
> Sometimes I feel like just throwing myself out into the world again and demanding of myself to just go ahead and have the attack. I am sick of worrying about when the big one will attack. I wish I could just wrestle it to the ground and beat the hell out of it.
>
> And for me to even talk like this is out of character. I am too nice, too patient, too religious, too kind, but on the other hand I'm not. I feel split down the middle. One part of me argues with the other part, and it leaves me feeling detached, not whole and I just want to integrate the two parts together and be strong. But I don't feel as though I can and I don't even know where to begin the process.

Most of us realise and acknowledge how negative our thoughts are, and we know at one level how our thoughts are creating our distress. But there is a 'gap' between knowing this and working effectively with our thinking. We can try various techniques — positive thinking, distraction techniques or realistic thinking — but many of us can't cross over the divide and stop the many and varied fears we have. We keep on getting caught back into the overall experience of our disorder. What we don't realise is that we have become players in the games of our mind.

And our mind can play many games. Our thoughts create all our feeling states — our happiness, sadness, anger, boredom, depression, excitement, irritability, hopefulness, helplessness, panic, anxiety, fear and *freedom*. We don't realise that we move in and out of various feeling states, guided by the way we are thinking. And we can move in and out of various feeling states from moment to moment.

One moment we can be feeling happy and a thought rises — 'I am feeling so good.' This is followed by another thought, 'How long will it last?' And we attach to the thought about our feelings of happiness not lasting, and we become anxious or depressed. Then we think, 'I knew it wouldn't last!' and we become attached to associated thoughts — 'Why does this always happen to me? Why can't I be happy?' We become a player in the mind games.

Anxiety game

I don't want to have another panic attack.
What's my heart rate?
This is not me, I'm not like this.
I hate feeling like this.
Why doesn't it just go away?
What if something does happen?
I feel so awful.
I shouldn't feel this way.
I can't keep feeling this way.
No one else could ever feel like this.
What if I do have one?
It's always too fast.
Why can't I recover?
I don't want to be like this.
I feel so horrible.
Why do I feel this way?
I can't feel like this.
Who wouldn't be anxious!
Why can't I stop this?
I can't cope.

What if . . . game

. . . the doctor has made a mistake?
. . . there really is something wrong?
. . . this isn't anxiety?
. . . I have an attack?
. . . I lose control?
. . . this isn't anxiety?
. . . I vomit?
. . . this is a brain tumour?
. . . I have a heart attack?
. . . I go insane?
. . . the next one is going to be the *one*?
. . . I make a fool of myself?
. . . I have an attack of diarrhoea?

. . . they see my hands shake?

. . . something happens?

. . . I blush?

. . . I never recover?

. . . I can't get to work?

. . . I have an attack in the car?

. . . I get home and there is no one there?

. . . the test results were mixed up?

. . . I get too dizzy, pass out or faint?

. . . no one is there to help me?

. . . perspire too much?

. . . people find out about me?

. . . I can get to work but have to leave?

. . . I can't get home?

. . . I can't get help?

Sleep game

I can't sleep.

How can I function tomorrow?

What if I wake up after a couple of hours?

I can't function if I can't get any sleep.

I am trying to sleep but can't.

Why can't I just fall asleep?

I am going to be so bad in the morning.

What will happen to me if I don't?

I have to get some sleep.

What if tonight is like last night?

What is going to happen?

I have to sleep.

Why isn't it happening?

I need my sleep.

How can I cope?

I have to make sure I go to sleep.

Mental abuse game

I am a failure.

I am weak.

I hate myself.

I should just be able to get it together.

I am to blame.

I am hopeless.

I am stupid, dumb.

Why can't I be strong?

I am angry at myself.

It's all my fault.

Checkmate game

I should.

I must.

I can't.

I should recover.

I shouldn't.

I have to.

I must do it perfectly.

I shouldn't feel like this.

I must recover.

I can't cope.

I have to recover.

I can't be selfish.

Guilt game

I shouldn't have done that.

I should have said yes.

I didn't mean to hurt their feelings.

I am such a bad person.

I shouldn't be angry.

I am letting everyone down.

I shouldn't have said that.

Why am I so selfish?

What if they misunderstood me?

I should have done better.

It is all my fault.

Why am I such a terrible person?

Victim game

I am worse than everyone else.

No one else is as bad as I am.

It is just not fair I am like this.

I can never recover.

I am a failure.

Why me?

What we don't realise is that this is how we think between our attacks, and this is what creates our anxiety and feelings of loss of control over our lives. But we haven't lost control, we have just become attached to our thoughts. And sometimes the remedies we try to stop the mind games become just another game.

Positive thinking games

GAME 1 AFFIRMATIONS

'Every day in every way I am getting better and better.'

We can write out this affirmation and put it on the bedroom mirror, on top of the television, in the hallway, on the refrigerator. In fact, we can wall-paper our whole house with this and similar messages. We are constantly reminded of it because it is everywhere. We repeat it to ourselves *ad nauseum*, but it doesn't work.

'Every day in every way we are getting sicker and sicker!'

because:

'Every day in every way I am getting better and better.' What's my pulse rate? Has it gone down? My heart is still racing. I hate feeling like this. Why doesn't it just go away? 'Every day in every way I am feeling better and better.' What if I have an attack? What if I have a heart attack? 'Every day in every way . . .'

GAME 2 POSITIVE THINKING VERSUS NEGATIVE THINKING

Although we can repeat affirmations and replace negative thoughts with positive ones we are still playing a mind game — the positive versus the negative. In fact, I feel that positive thinking can be as destructive as negative thinking. Most of us do not believe the 'positive' because of the way we perceive our attacks, panic and anxiety.

'I feel fantastic.' No, you feel terrible. 'I feel great.' Are you kidding? You feel horrible. 'I know today is going to be a wonderful day.' For you or for your anxiety? 'I am never going to panic again.' Want to bet?

Distraction game

'I am feeling really anxious. I can't feel like this. I'll count to twenty. One, two, three . . . that isn't working. I'll concentrate really hard on this book I'm reading. No, that isn't working, I feel horrible. I'll watch television. No, I still feel awful. I will go for a walk, smell the roses, so to speak. But what if I have a panic attack on the way?'

While some people can use distraction techniques, they don't last. Nor do they bridge the gap of knowing and working effectively with our thinking, because we are not dealing with the root cause of our distress, and that is the thoughts themselves.

Realistic thinking game

This can also happen sometimes using other cognitive techniques, such as realistic thinking. With this technique we write down our thoughts and find the evidence that proves or disproves the thought, and then write down a more realistic thought.

Thought: 'I am going to go insane.'

Where is the evidence that proves this? 'I haven't. Yet.'

Where is the evidence that proves I won't? 'My doctor and other people say that I won't. No one goes insane through an anxiety disorder. But are they really sure?'

Realistic thought: 'My panic and anxiety will not send me insane. Well, at least I hope it won't.'

The analysis game

We can write down all our thoughts. In fact, we can fill book after book with our thoughts. And we can analyse them, and analyse them, and become trapped in analysis paralysis, and round and round we go, as an unwilling participant in yet another game.

'Look at all these thoughts. Why am I thinking like this? Why am I having these thoughts. There has to be a reason. What's wrong with me? The answer has to be in here somewhere. Why can't I work out why I am thinking like this? It is driving me crazy. I hate this. Why is this happening to me? Why doesn't it just stop and go away? It is non-stop, over and over again. Why am I thinking like this? "Every day in every way . . . one, two, three." I can't find the evidence that I won't go insane!'

From: Karen

SUBJECT: THOUGHT CATCHER

The panic attacks I've had in the past were violent and seemed to last a long time, several hours in fact. I am getting to the point where the anxiety doesn't bug me too much, but the thought of a violent panic attack still does.

I may not be right about this, but from experience I can say that the violent attacks I've had during this disorder always took a lot of preparation! In other words, I was usually all worked up about one thing or another for a while before the attack, sometimes days before.

I was always worrying, obsessing, or just plain thinking the worst. This behaviour always led up to the violent and long-lasting attacks. The tiny surge attacks and/or the little quickie attacks, ten minutes and under, seemed to come more spontaneously, but never the long violent ones. So how can we help prevent these long violent attacks from happening?

If you look back at some of the bad attacks you've had, try to see what it was you were doing to yourself with your thoughts in the days or hours before the attack, and also what you were telling yourself during the attack, which keeps it going longer. I'm sure you'll see a pattern. Try to catch yourself thinking the thoughts that bring on these attacks before they build up. Again, it's working with the thoughts, not just during an attack, not just during a practice session in the stores, but all day, every day. Since I've been doing this, I haven't had one of the long-lasting attacks at all.

CHAPTER 8

MINDFULNESS

> **From: Karen**
> **SUBJECT: WHAT IF? SO WHAT!**
> I can see it all. It's not the symptoms that matter, it's what I make of them that creates the disorder. This last experience has shown me how completely catastrophic my thinking is, and not just with the symptoms but in every area of my life, from my health, to relationships, to my future. What I'm taking into every situation from now on is the simple phrase I have up on my computer: 'Change Your Perception.'

Karen is exactly right! The way we are thinking is creating our anxiety and panic symptoms. When we fear our symptoms or try to stop them, all we are doing is creating more.

We are not aware of the enormous power that our thoughts have. It is our thoughts that generate our feelings and emotions. We don't recognise how we can be happy one moment, anxious the next, feeling guilty in the next, while feeling helpless in the next. We simply don't recognise the power of thought and how our thoughts dictate the feeling quality of our life. We simply attach to our thoughts from the moment we wake in the morning, and we stay caught up in them until we go to sleep at night.

When we begin to meditate we become much more aware of our thoughts. As our meditation deepens, we become aware and see how our thoughts are not an endless stream, but rise independently of each other. A thought rises into consciousness and, if we don't attach to it, it will subside. Another thought will rise, then subside. This is the nature of our mind — the rising and falling away of thoughts. Like the rising of a wave in the ocean, the wave peaks and then dissolves back into the ocean.

We don't let our thoughts dissolve. We attach to them and we are carried along with the tide, not realising that our thoughts are constantly rising and falling away. We are a player in the games of our mind, and we are not aware how these games determine the affective quality of our life.

Changing our perception

From: Martha
SUBJECT: HAMMERING IT HOME
I think the main point that Vicki and Bronwyn both try to make is not to buy into these symptoms. They are transitory. One of the hardest things to accept is that we are doing this to ourselves; with our own thoughts of all things.

I suppose if I repeatedly banged myself over the head with a hammer I'd be told that was the reason for me getting a headache. But first I would have to see the hammer, and watch my own hand as I hammered away. This is in essence where true recovery lies, to see how our own thinking creates our disorder.

If we read through all the mind games we play, we can see how we are not dealing with the current moment. We miss the current moment, because we are either thinking of past experiences or projecting them into the future — which, incidentally, is only a moment away. As Karen says in the email on p. 103, she was constantly living in a future filled with anxiety and panic with no relief in sight.

To begin to work with our thinking, we need to come to the current moment and work with our disorder, as it is in this moment. Let's come back to basics. When we had our first few attacks, or began to experience high levels of anxiety, we were frightened and confused. We did not know what was happening to us, and that is completely understandable. It is a terrifying experience.

But now we know what is happening to us. We have had all the necessary clinical tests and we have been diagnosed as having an anxiety disorder.

It doesn't mean we are having a heart attack, nor does it mean we are going to die, or go insane or lose control in some way. It means we are having panic attacks and/or anxiety. This is how we are supposed to feel when we have them. Nothing more, nothing less. This is the reality of our experience at this moment in time.

Yet we are not dealing with them in this moment. Nor are we dealing with them as they really are. We draw on our past experiences of our attacks, anxiety and the feelings of terror, and project them into the future, whether that be in the next moment or five minutes or five days or more away.

The first step in changing our perception is for us to *begin again* in this moment. To do this, we need to let go of our past experiences of our attacks and anxiety and the numerous fears we may have. We will not be able to 'begin again' if we use our past experiences as a frame of reference, because this is already determining our future. We can change the future by changing our 'frame of reference' — that is, the way we perceive our attacks and anxiety. We let go of past experiences and begin again right now in this moment.

In building a new frame of reference, we bring into this moment the fact that our major panic and anxiety fears have not happened, nor will they happen as a result of panic and anxiety. We may occasionally have felt embarrassed or felt we had made a fool of ourselves, but nothing has happened to us.

Our lives as we knew them may have been destroyed by our anxiety disorder, but they have been destroyed more by our perception of our panic attacks and anxiety than by the actual experience of them. If we didn't fear them, if we weren't playing mind games, we would not be experiencing the distress that we do. We need to begin again, and learn to understand why our major panic and anxiety fears will not happen now or in the future.

We need to be mindful of our thoughts, and we need to become aware of how our thoughts are creating our feeling states. In this instance, if we experience panic disorder we need to become aware of:

- any ability to dissociate;
- how this in turn can trigger an attack;

- how our thoughts about this triggers the fight-or-flight response;
- which creates our feelings of panic and anxiety.

If we experience one of the other anxiety disorders we need to become aware of:

- how our thoughts trigger the fight-or-flight response;
- which creates our feelings of panic and anxiety.

When we can see how our experience is being created, we realise why there is nothing to fear. Our perception of our experience changes. Our attitude towards our symptoms changes. We see this not just at an intellectual level but, most importantly, we see it at an emotional level. When we can see and *feel* how it is all being created, we lose our fear, because we understand it and we understand why it will not hurt us. When we can see and *feel* the truth of this at an emotional level, we can become the umpire of the mind games, instead of a player.

Beginning again

In meditation we learn to become aware of when we are attaching to our thoughts, rather than focusing on the object of meditation. We bring this same principle into everyday life, except that this time we will not be meditating. We simply become mindful of the process of our thoughts and the feeling states that arise from these thoughts. Becoming mindful means we separate ourselves from our thoughts, we step back from our thoughts, and simply watch them. At this stage we become a spectator, not a player in the game. We observe our thoughts, we witness our thoughts.

We need to observe the whole thought process. When we feel anxious we don't see the thought that turned on the fight-or-flight response. Instead we go immediately to the feeling of being anxious, and think anxiously about it. We don't see the mind state that originally created it, because we have become caught up, attached to, the very act of thinking. In becoming mindful we break our attachment to the thinking process and simply become aware of the process itself.

From: Karen

SUBJECT: WILL I EVER BE OVER THIS ANXIETY DISORDER?

I woke up again this morning with the ever familiar morning anxiety and initially just wanted to cry, and I did actually cry a little. I now see that I have such a tendency to look days, weeks, years ahead and completely overwhelm myself into anxiety and worry. I need to work on taking things day by day, moment by moment, thought by thought. I'm always way ahead of myself, ahead of my life, wondering how on earth I'll ever cope, manage it all, any crisis and the ups and downs. Then I feel inadequate, unable to cope and, bang, anxiety city. No wonder I have been so trapped for so long. I have been absolutely paralysing myself by living in the future. And, of course, it is a future filled with problems, naturally.

Instead of just living my life day to day I have been constantly thinking in terms of 'Oh, will I ever be over this anxiety disorder? How will I take care of myself?' And I actually wonder why I am so anxious!

I have never realised how often I do this to myself. Looking back even at the ten years I was anxiety and panic free, I can see how horrible I've been to myself. How I have terrorised myself with the 'what ifs' and the fears. How I've held myself back, limited myself, scared myself, told myself I wasn't good enough. It scares me to think I've done this most of my life. So back to the lab, Igor. More work to do. One thought at a time.

Mindfulness

We need to be aware, we need to be mindful of what we are thinking about. We need to watch the moment-to-moment passing parade of our thoughts. It is not a matter of analysing them or wondering why we are thinking like this. It is not a matter of telling ourselves, I shouldn't think this. We need to be mindful and we need to be non-judgmental. The more mindful we can become, the more we will begin to see the dynamics of our whole experience.

As we begin to practise becoming mindful, it is very easy for us to forget about being aware and attach back into our thoughts. This is where we need to become disciplined and it can be helpful if we use reminders throughout the day to assist us in becoming aware of what are we thinking about.

Notice what you are thinking of when you:

- wake in the morning;
- have breakfast;
- begin the day;
- take the children to school;
- leave for work;
- see a bus;
- see a red car on the road;
- hear the phone ring;
- have morning tea;
- have lunch;
- have afternoon tea;
- come home;
- have dinner;
- go for a walk;
- have a drink;
- prepare a meal;
- feed your pets;
- wash the dishes;
- before social occasions;
- during social occasions;
- after social occasions;
- before business meetings;
- during meetings;
- after meetings;
- help children with homework;
- settle the children for the night;
- watch television;
- turn on the computer;
- get ready for bed.

What are you thinking about right now?

We need to listen to our thoughts. Become aware of the mind games. Become aware of the incessant internal conversations. Something may have happened, or could happen, or shouldn't happen. Watch the thoughts as they weave various conversations, various outcomes, round and round.

Become aware of how you 'switch' on the radar first thing in the morning to see if your symptoms are awake. And, of course, they are, because the moment you turn on the 'radar' they are ready for the day's action!

Dissociation

If you have any of the dissociative symptoms listed in Chapter 4, become aware of how they are happening. How did you move into a trance state?

- Were you staring?
- What were you staring at:
  - out of the window?
  - while driving the car?

- stopped at a red light?
- the car in front of you?
- the road ahead of you?
- the computer?
- the television?
- a book?
- Were you talking with someone?
- Were you day-dreaming?
  - if so, how 'deep' was the day-dream state?
- Were you totally self-absorbed in your thinking?
- Were you under fluorescent lights?

The more aware we become, the more we will recognise the sequence of events that lead to our overall experience.

DISSOCIATION WITHOUT AN ATTACK
dissociative/trance state → thoughts → fight-or-flight response → panic anxiety symptoms → thoughts

DISSOCIATION WITH AN ATTACK
dissociation → attack → thoughts → fight-or-flight response → panic anxiety symptoms → thoughts

NOCTURNAL ATTACK
attack → thoughts → fight-or-flight response → panic and anxiety symptoms → thoughts

PANIC ATTACKS WITHOUT DISSOCIATION
thoughts → fight-or-flight response → panic and anxiety symptoms → thoughts

ANXIETY
thoughts → fight-or-flight response → symptoms → thoughts

Mindfulness checklist 1

DISSOCIATIVE/TRANCE STATES

- What were you doing before you dissociated?
- How did you dissociate?
- What were you thinking about when you did dissociate?
- What happened the moment you tranced out? What did you think?
- Did you have an attack while dissociating?
- Did you panic? If so, what were you thinking about?

PANIC ATTACKS/ANXIETY

- What were you thinking about just before your last panic attack?
- What were you thinking about during your last panic attack?
- What were you thinking about after your last panic attack?
- What were you thinking about before your anxiety peaked to higher levels?
- What were you thinking about after your anxiety peaked to higher levels?
- What are you thinking about when you are chronically anxious every waking moment?
- What were you thinking about as you woke up this morning?
- What were you thinking about as you went to sleep last night?
- What were you thinking about shortly before you realised you were feeling depressed?
- What did you think about when you realised you were feeling depressed?
- Do you become depressed because you are feeling depressed?
- What thoughts created the depression over the depression?

Handy hint number 552. The answer to all the above is not 'I wasn't thinking of anything or doing anything!' You were! You are just not aware.

When we attach to our thoughts we don't recognise that we are thinking, because we are caught up in the very act of thinking. There is no separation between thinker and thought. And so we lose the clarity of what is actually happening in the present moment. We allow a mental process to dictate the way we feel, not just in the present moment but also into the future.

In the initial stages of becoming mindful, we get caught up time and time again in our dissociation and in our thoughts and before we know it we are panicking or highly anxious. We need to become disciplined in becoming mindful. It is very important that we become aware of the intimate connection between our dissociation and our attack and/or of the connection between our thoughts and feelings of panic and anxiety. If we don't see this connection, then we can still be fearful of our whole experience.

We need to be more aware of how our experience is being created, moment to moment. And when we can see this both intellectually and *emotionally*, we realise there is nothing to be afraid of and our fears dissolve. It was the play of our mind.

From: Group member
SUBJECT: AWARENESS

I am so aware of how I hook into my thoughts. I watched it happening all night last night. I knew it was happening, but couldn't find the mind set to stop it. A negative thought popped in, and I felt my heart sink before I could say, 'Just a thought, let it go,' and then I thought, 'Damn, you've just given it power!!' And it came up and up and up relentlessly. I know exactly why they reoccur and bother me and why my heart sinks. It's still the fear of having the thoughts. Some I do buy into before I can help myself, and then they wind up with the power.

I'm aware that the same one will not stay in my mind all the time, that it does eventually go and that's a good realisation. However, my thoughts can be triggered by various situations including sight or a sound. I say to myself, 'I can choose what I want to think about,' but when I say to myself, 'Okay, let's have some positive images here, let's have some fun, let's just notice the beautiful snow outside,' up pops the thought, 'You can't choose.'

I am aware that I am thinking this, but I still get caught up in it. I get overwhelmed with their constancy and negativity. The next thing I know, is that I feel I want to run from my own head stuff. I am wanting to leave awareness alone and just hope my thoughts will eventually go away on their own.

It feels like I can't have a natural nice experience or a pleasant thought, if my awareness of my thoughts constantly brings this stuff up. But I don't want to let the awareness go because I can *feel* the truth in all this. I just can't seem to get it to stick in my head that my thoughts are totally harmless no matter if they pop up a thousand times a day. The day this happens I'll be ecstatic!

From: Bronwyn

SUBJECT: AWARENESS

The reason why your thoughts come so relentlessly is because you are attaching to them, by thinking you shouldn't have these thoughts! It doesn't matter if you have a negative thought. You are going to. We all do. The secret is not to worry if you do. When we judge our thoughts as being 'negative', we give our power away. It is the judgment that does the damage: 'Why am I thinking like this? Why doesn't it go away? What do I have to do to stop it?' When we think like this we begin a new game called, 'I shouldn't think like this!'

Just watch the play of the mind. Be aware of the play of the mind. Don't judge it. Simply watch the rise and fall of thoughts. Anxiety thought, panic thought, depressive thought, negative thought, happy thought, curious thought. Labelling is not judging. We just watch the play of the mind as we would watch a street parade. Clowns, marching band, marching girls, people dressed in various costumes. We watch the parade, but we don't take part in it. And this is what we need to do with our thoughts. Just watch them pass by. Nor is there any reason to fear our thoughts. See them for what they are — thoughts, just the play of the mind.

It is great that you realise your thoughts do disappear and you can build on this. They only stay in our mind because we keep them there by attaching to them. When you can detach from them and simply watch them, they will disappear far faster.

And you are right, we can also get caught up with a thousand and one associations, conditioning, sights, smells, all of this, but this is what the mind does. This is how it keeps reinventing itself moment to moment. It's just the mind at play.

Trying to replace 'negative' thoughts with 'positive' ones or trying to distract is just changing the rules of this particular mind game. And the mind will not allow you to do that. After all, it makes the rules of its games! So you need just to become a spectator and simply watch from the side-lines. When you don't hook into the thoughts they simply rise and then disappear.

Awareness doesn't bring up 'stuff'. It is the attaching to thoughts that gives rise to other thoughts. You also need to realise that, when you become aware, you actually see the whole process for the first time. These thoughts have always been around, but now you are seeing them. And, yes, people can become very frightened of seeing the content of their thoughts. They will push them away, turn off their awareness and think, 'I can't think about this, I don't want to know this.' But what happens? They are still there and still creating the problem. Being frightened of them, not wanting to know about them, is just another mind game.

In one way, it is because you do feel the truth in all of this that you are attaching to them. It is as though you are trying to 'get back to the truth of it' by fearing the fact that you are having negative thoughts. This will keep the truth at arm's length. Let the truth come naturally by simply watching your thoughts and not getting involved with them.

Mindfulness checklist 2

- What is the relationship between any ability to dissociate and your attack sensations?
- What is the relationship between your thoughts and your anxiety, panic, depression?
- Can you see how your thoughts are creating the fear?
- Can you see how your body reacts to the fear?
- Can you see why there is nothing to be frightened of?
- What difficulties are you having?
- Are you having difficulty in becoming aware?
- Are you attaching to all your thoughts?
- Are you frightened of your thoughts?
- Do you think 'I can't do this'?
- Do you think this is all too hard?
- Do you feel your thoughts are racing too fast to do this?
- Are you thinking 'I shouldn't be thinking like this'?

These are just thoughts! Step back and simply watch your thoughts parade by.

Letting go

From: Martha

SUBJECT: WORRISOME THOUGHTS

Last week I had to go to the doctor for a routine check-up and they did a blood work-up thing. Of course, the results took a week. Last night the nurse calls and tells me the results are in, but he can't give me the results because the doctor wanted to speak with me and he wouldn't be in until later today. Talk about horror. It gave me a raging headache. I was a basket case. Finally, at 8.30 this evening, Doctor Scaremetodeath finally called and said everything was fine except for my cholesterol.

But to be honest, today while waiting for him to call, I finally decided that enough is enough and I have to stop letting those worrisome thoughts control me. Every time a thought would come up I'd look at it, identify it as absurd and let it go. Naturally, I am exhausted because this has been practically every waking moment of my day. But it does help.

When we learn to become mindful, we separate ourselves from our thoughts. Instead of attaching to them, we simply observe them. We see how our thoughts turn on the fight-or-flight response, and we see how our symptoms are being created. As we become more familiar with the overall relationship between our thoughts and symptoms, we realise that we actually have a choice in what we think about.

We know that if we keep on with a particular thought pattern we will become a player in a mind game that can lead to anxiety, panic or depression. We can choose either to keep on thinking the thoughts, or we can choose to let them go. And to do this we draw on the meditation technique again.

In meditation we are aware when we become involved with our thoughts, and we let the thoughts go, and we bring our mind back to the object of our meditation. In everyday living we change this slightly. While we will still be letting go of our thoughts, we will not be bringing our mind back to a word, mantra or the breath. Instead, we label the thought and we let it go.

We label our thoughts for three reasons. We do this so that we can begin to recognise the various types of thoughts that we have, and the various mind games we play. This assists us to recognise the team players before the game starts!

And in labelling the thought, we break our attachment to the thought. We take ourselves out of the game. When we exercise our choice and choose not to become involved in a particular thought pattern, we become the umpire of the game, not a player!

The third reason that we label our thoughts is to prevent us from distracting from them. When we label the thought, we acknowledge it. We are not 'running' from it. This can happen when we distract from our thoughts. If we distract, we are not given the opportunity to understand exactly how our thoughts are creating our experience. Nor does it give us an opportunity to change our thought patterns.

1. We become aware of our thoughts but we choose not to think them and so we label the thought — or, if you prefer, label the 'game'.

anxiety	panic	depression
guilt	victim	what will people think
frustration	negative	mental abuse

Label the thought: don't run from it, avoid it, change it, analyse it or judge it. When we do any of these, all we are doing is giving our thoughts the power and we become caught up in yet another game.

Our group member was recognising her thoughts but she was judging her thoughts as 'negative' and became attached to the thought 'Why am I thinking like this?' Labelling our thoughts is not judging, it is acknowledging them. Judging our thoughts is fear-based. Labelling our thoughts enables us to let them go more easily. When we judge our thoughts, it is difficult to let them go.

2. Once we label the thought, we simply let it go as we do in meditation.

We *do not* bring our mind back to a word, mantra or breath. Instead, we become involved in labelling our thoughts and letting them go. The moment we label our thoughts and let them go, they will come straight back. We let that thought go and it will come up again immediately. We label it and let it go.

We need to remember that our mind is not disciplined but runs free — free to create havoc in our lives! It is not going to hand over the control to us easily. In the beginning our thoughts win. We will attach to them and get caught up in the game time and time again. And so we do need patience. We are training our thoughts to play a different game, one in which we are not an unwitting player but rather the umpire!

In time, with practice and discipline our thoughts will rise into consciousness and automatically disappear without our need to let them go. At this stage we will have total and complete power over our thoughts. If we want to think about something, we consciously choose to. Otherwise, our thoughts disappear without any effort on our part.

Letting it happen

From: Karen
SUBJECT: IRONY

I can see now that the very things we do to 'protect' ourselves from panic and anxiety are the things that actually bring it on, keep it going. The thing we are most afraid to do, let go — give up trying to control it — is the one thing that sets us free. It's ironic. The way out of this disorder is what we are all so afraid to do. *Let go* and *let it happen.* Am I on the right track here??

Yes, Karen is on the right track. Becoming aware of the relationship between our dissociation and our thoughts, and/or our thoughts and our panic, anxiety symptoms, shows us very clearly how our distress is being created. The more we understand this, the more our perception of our experience changes, and it becomes easier to stop playing the mind games.

As we are learning to be aware of our thoughts and learning to let them go, we will still have symptoms because we will be getting caught up in our thoughts. Our next step is taking back our power, by letting our attacks, panic and anxiety happen. This means we stop fighting them.

When we don't know or understand what is happening to us, it is only natural we fight it. But now that we do know, we need to stop *fighting* it. Notice I have highlighted the word 'fighting'. This only makes the situation worse. When we fight and resist our symptoms we keep the fight-or-flight response activated.

We fight it mentally — Oh no, not again. I hate this. I can't stand it. Why doesn't it go away?

We fight it by monitoring — Where is it? What's my heart rate? Are my hands shaking?

We fight it physically — we hold our breath, tense our muscles, clench our fists or our jaw.

But what is our fighting doing? Is it helping us in any way? No, of course not. If fighting it was going to stop it, we wouldn't have a disorder in the first place!

From: Martha

SUBJECT: THIS TOO WILL PASS

I think if we can just learn not to let the feelings double and triple in power, then the first wave will pass. The hard part is learning how not to panic when we feel the first wave. I am really working on just letting it wash over me and then letting go. So much easier said than done, because the feeling is so overwhelming, and, of course, that is where our own personal power comes in.

We have to remind ourselves that this isn't dangerous or fatal. It is merely a feeling and feelings pass if we allow them to. I now know that one of the reasons my panic attacks were so violent is because I fought them so hard. It felt as though some entity had crawled inside me and wouldn't let go. Naturally, I fought back as I thought I was fighting for my life.

We need to let our symptoms 'wash over us', as Martha says. Or, quoting from Martha again, we need to let them 'roll through like a summer storm'. We need to let our symptoms happen without fighting them.

To do this, we come back to the practice of meditation. We have already brought over from our meditation practice the skills of being aware and of letting go of our thoughts. Now we need to bring over the skill of letting ourselves feel whatever it is we are feeling. In meditation we simply let whatever happens, happen. We don't fight it in any way. We don't resist it in any way. Nor do we control it in any way. We just let it happen. And we also need to bring this skill into our everyday life.

If we dissociate, then it is a matter of being aware *how* we are dissociating, of breaking our stare, breaking our gaze, breaking our self-absorption and letting go of any fearful thoughts about it. *So what!*

If we have an attack we need to let it happen, to do whatever it wants to do. If we have an electric shock move through our body, then we let it move through. If we have the sensation of burning heat or a burning tingling heat, a vibration or unusual energies moving through the body, then we let it happen. *So what!* If we are woken from sleep with a nocturnal attack, all it means is that it has woken us. Let it happen, 'so what', and roll over and go back to sleep.

We simply don't resist it or fight whatever we experience. We give into it. Instead of 'what if' we need to see it for what it is. *So what!*

When we are having a panic attack which has been induced by our thoughts, we let the panic attack happen without fighting it or resisting it. If we feel anxious, we let ourselves feel anxious. If we are hyperventilating, then we break the hyperventilation as I describe in Chapter 4.

Once we have been told by our doctor there is nothing wrong with our heart, and if our heart is racing through the anxiety, we simply note it, 'heart racing', and we let it race. If we are feeling nauseous, then we let ourselves feel nauseous; if we are going to be sick, then we let ourselves be sick. If we are going to have an attack of diarrhoea, then we have an attack of diarrhoea. If we need to urinate, then we need to urinate. If our hands are shaking, then our hands are shaking. If our face is flushed, then our face is flushed, if we are perspiring, then we are perspiring. If we feel as if we are going to faint, then we sit down, on a chair, on the floor or on the footpath if need be.

I know what you are thinking! After this session in the workshops, people queue up to say to me in hushed whispers 'I can't let it happen. What would people think? I am a nurse/teacher/CEO/lawyer/marketing manager/bank officer/waiter/cashier/student. What would people say? They can't see me have an attack, I can't let my hands shake, I can't be sick, I can't have an attack of diarrhoea, I can't have a flushed face, I can't be soaked through with perspiration!'

Why not? If it means you recover, *so what!*

As Karen says in Chapter 3: 'What will others think or say if I panic?? Arghhh!!! Who gives a hoot what they think? I can live now. Today. Because if panic is so harmless, and has nothing to do with insanity or competence, if it's not going to make me pass out, have a heart attack, why the heck am I still tip-toeing through my life? Fear of criticism or rejection? Who cares! I think I have finally grasped the meaning of *so what!* and it is more profound and deeper than I could ever have imagined.'

It doesn't matter what other people think. Think about it. Our mental health needs to be more important than what we think other people are thinking! Our recovery needs to be our number one priority. Many of us are the greatest actors in the world. No one would know if we are having an attack or feeling anxious. We are experts in being able to hide it. But how much energy does it take to do this? It takes an enormous amount, and all this does is keep the fight-or-flight response going.

We don't realise when we are worrying about what other people think that they may not be thinking about us at all. Suppose you are in a supermarket. You see two of your friends walking towards you, smiling. You think to yourself, 'Oh no. I don't want to talk to anyone. I just feel so awful.' You exchange pleasantries. You ask how they are and they give you the automatic polite response; they ask you how you are and you reply, 'I don't know. I am having such a difficult time with this anxiety. When I saw you I thought I might have a panic attack because I haven't got the energy to try and hide it.'

They will usually respond in one of two ways: 'That's good. Glad you are feeling okay.' They simply don't hear you! They are on automatic pilot. They are hearing what they expect to hear, that you are fine. Don't you always say that? What we don't realise is that people have their own worries and problems and, like us, can be so engrossed in thinking their own thoughts they simply don't hear us.

Or they may reply, 'Really, I had that a while ago', or 'That's what I have.' We hide it from other people, and my rule of thumb is: three people that we know are hiding it from us for the same reasons we are hiding it from them: 'What will they think of me?'

From: Margaret
SUBJECT: WHAT WILL PEOPLE THINK?
It's funny, isn't it, that people don't notice? Well, none of my friends and family do anyway. I get the same thing — 'Oh, you are so calm and in control, Margaret.' LOL.

The people I think that notice my fear are strangers, because they are the people I feel it most with, even though I can be anxious around my family.

I can see my face in my mind's eye. Those 'rabbit in the headlights' eyes, the red face, the terror. Good imagination if nothing else!! I should put my vivid imagination to better use.

Our mental health is more important than what we perceive other people's opinions to be. The irony is, the harder we fight our experience the more we fuel it. There is more chance of someone finding out, or seeing physical signs of it, when we fight it. When we let it happen, we turn off the fight-or-flight response and the attack is over as quickly as it started. Instead of 'what if' it becomes *so what!*.

We just let it happen. We don't need to become involved with it. When we are feeling happy what do we do? Do we monitor our body for happiness? My head is happy. My throat is happy, my heart is happy, my stomach is happy, my bowel is happy, my bladder is happy. Of course we don't. We simply note we are happy and get on with what we are doing. (As long as we are not thinking, 'How long will this last?')

The same applies to our panic and anxiety. We don't need to become caught up in it, or caught up in the thoughts that created it. We choose not to become involved with our thoughts, we validate them, let them go and let our symptoms happen.

What we don't realise is, when we let the anxiety and our attacks happen the only thing that happens to us is we recover! When we let it happen and don't buy into it with our thinking, when we don't resist it, we turn off the fight-or-flight response and it stops. It is over, because there is nothing to fuel it — unless we think to ourselves 'what if?'

It can be frightening the first time we let it happen. Frightening because we are taking our major fears head on, but we allow ourselves to feel frightened and let it happen! *So what!*

To summarise:

- We need to become aware of any ability to dissociate.
- If we have dissociated we need to break it as I have outlined above.
- We need to become aware, to be mindful of our thoughts.
- We need to be mindful of how our body reacting to our thoughts.
- We need to be aware we have a choice in what we think about.
- We can keep thinking our thoughts, or we can label them and let them go.
- And we let our attacks, panic and anxiety happen.

Are you having difficulty letting your thoughts go? Do you:

- find you are constantly getting caught up in your thoughts?
- think you will never be able to control them?
- think your thoughts have a life of their own?
- think it all seems too difficult?

Remember, these are also just thoughts!

Recovery with attitude

From: Martha and Angie
SUBJECT: ANGER
What do we do with this anger when we feel it come up?
Bronwyn says that we get mad at the disorder, but that feels like I am mad at myself and I can't figure out how to do this.

From: Margaret
SUBJECT: ANGER
I haven't got to this stage yet. I still feel like a victim when I have a panic attack, so the best I can do is to weakly plead, 'Go away you nasty thing you. Please, pretty please go away.' But I'm working up to the 'F' technique.

From: Bronwyn

SUBJECT: ANGER

Our anger is far more powerful than our anxiety and panic and it can really be the rocket-ship to recovery. We all have problems experiencing our anger, this is part of the reason why we have developed the disorder in the first place! But there comes a time, as we are working through the recovery process, that we do feel angry. Angry at being mindful and very angry about labelling and letting go of our thoughts. We think to ourselves, enough is enough! We need to direct our anger to our thoughts, our symptoms, and to everything associated with our disorder.

Being angry at ourselves will only create further anxiety and panic. We need to separate our self from our anxiety disorder. We are not an anxiety disorder. We are a person who has one. It is happening to us. It is like a person with a broken leg. They don't turn into a broken leg. They have a broken leg.

I say this because sometimes it is difficult to see this separation, because we can be so caught up in it all. Same with our thoughts. Our thoughts are now part and parcel of the disorder. They are not us. We can separate ourselves from them.

Get angry at the thoughts which create it, get angry at the anxiety, panic, and the avoidance behaviour. Think about it. How dare it do this to you? How dare it destroy your life? Enough is enough is enough. Tell it where to go in whatever language you feel comfortable with. For me it was what one psychiatrist calls Bronwyn's 'F' technique!!

Why aren't we angry? Our disorder can take over and destroy our life as we knew it. We can hate our disorder, but no matter how much we 'hate' it we are still passive in our response to it. Why? Think about this. Anger is a healthy response to what is happening to us. If someone broke into our home and stole our most treasured possessions would our reaction be a passive one? Would be blame ourselves? Or would we be angry?

- Why aren't you angry at your disorder?
- Are you frightened to feel the anger?
- Are you directing the anger back onto yourself or other people?
- Do you think that if you get angry you will lose control?
- Do you think that you are not an angry person so you can't get angry?
- Why aren't you angry about what has happened to you?

When we are angry and we direct it onto our disorder, we need to do it with power. Not 'Go away, I am angry at you' but 'GO AWAY!' or words to that effect! Feel the full extent of your anger and feel its power. You will know when you are doing it the right way, because your anxiety and panic will disappear so fast that it can be frightening! But don't buy into that game! Same with your thoughts. Tell them in no uncertain terms what to do.

From: Angie
SUBJECT: WHY NOT?
Challenging the anxiety was a new experience for me but it was very empowering. I realised last night that you have to challenge it over and over again, every time it comes up. I thought that if you challenged it once, it would go away for good. LOL. Now I know that's just not the case. I think you just have to get so fed up with the anxiety and everything it represents that you just finally tell it where to go.

From: Karen
SUBJECT: WHY NOT?
This is the way I've been approaching things these last few days. I say to it, 'Okay, if I drop dead, I drop dead. So what. Just get it over with already.' Works every time!

CHAPTER 9

PEELING THE ONION

From: Martha
SUBJECT: RECOVERY

I am just trying to figure out how to put all this into some kind of order in my head where it finally makes sense. I get bits and pieces, but it is yet to totally sink in.

From: Karen
SUBJECT: RECOVERY

I think the recovery process is like a jigsaw puzzle. First we open the box and look at all those tiny pieces. Eeeek! We wonder if we really want to start this project, or if we should just put it away for now. If we decide to start working on it, first we have to empty out the box, turn over all the pieces, maybe look for all the ones with a straight edge to make the border and give us something to work with. The rest of the pieces fall into place slowly and sometimes you can't put one in, unless you already have a few of the others in the same area. The pieces are like our insights, our realisations and our work on our self. Only when several pieces fit into place in an area do we feel like we are making any progress, but in actuality each and every tiny piece we work with is leading up to the finished design. Recovery! You have the border in place and now you're just working on filling in the middle.

Skilful compassionate action

The border of the 'puzzle' represents our commitment to ourselves with all this entails:

- being open to the idea of caring for and accepting ourselves as we are;
- becoming responsible for ourselves;
- accepting our anxiety disorder;
- understanding our disorder;
- becoming disciplined in meditation or relaxation;
- developing mindfulness skills.

Filling in the middle of the puzzle is the process of working through to recovery:

- learning to manage our panic attacks and anxiety on a daily basis;
- working with our avoidance behaviour;
- working through any prescribed-drug addiction or alcohol dependency;
- choosing to work through any unresolved past or current personal issues, including any history of childhood abuse;
- choosing to work towards building our self-esteem.

I use the word 'choose' in the last two points. Some people will go on to work with their self-esteem issues and, if applicable, any history of childhood abuse, but other people prefer not to. There is no right or wrong way. The bottom line is doing what we feel is most beneficial for us as individuals. But if we don't work with the first three points, we will not learn to manage our attacks and anxiety!

Threshold to stress

From: Karen
SUBJECT: THRESHOLD TO STRESS
Before this disorder I used to be able to handle anything without getting upset or anxious. Now my threshold to stress is practically zero. I feel like I can't handle the daily tasks of life. I am worried that my tolerance to stress will always be this low and I don't want that to happen.

From: Vicki

SUBJECT: THRESHOLD TO STRESS

No. It won't always be this low. It is a bit like 'running on empty'. You will begin to build your tolerance back to higher levels through:

Being kind to yourself, meditating, working with mindfulness during the day, making sure you're eating properly and getting enough sleep.

You also need to begin to extend the mindfulness technique so that you can begin to identify the sources of stress in your life and make the necessary decisions about them.

Our disorders are a reaction to stress. As I've said, this doesn't mean we are weak. It doesn't mean we are a failure. It means we reached our threshold to stress and, when we did, our panic attacks and anxiety were triggered. Other people react to stress in other ways, including developing high blood pressure or migraines. Our anxiety disorder is the particular way we react. And is it any wonder why we do?

Most people with an anxiety disorder feel that they shouldn't be affected by major stresses or any other stressful period in their life. They feel as if they should be able to handle 'it' effortlessly. This is not skilful or compassionate!

When I ask people what happened in their life prior to developing an anxiety disorder, they will usually list a number of major stressful events. Some of these may go back six to twelve months before their disorder was triggered.

One woman listed a number of events in the past year. A family member had died; she and her partner had bought a new house; she had been retrenched from her employment a couple of months later; their children were having difficulty adjusting to a new suburb and school; and her partner had been injured in a car accident. When I asked her if she could see the relationship between these events and the development of her panic attacks, she replied that she should have been able to deal with all of it without it affecting her!

We all expect nothing less from ourselves, and then we can't understand why we develop a disorder. We feel we should just get on with it all, and 'get on with it all' as perfectly as possible.

Would you expect other people to deal with major stress without any effect? Do you tell them they are weak or a failure? Would you tell them they should pull themselves together so they can be strong for other people? Would you say this to someone else? No, of course not. So why are you expecting this of yourself?

The first layer

As we become more mindful we will see very clearly the unrealistic expectations and demands we place upon ourselves. Not only do these create stress, these expectations and demands are also part of the way we deal with stress, whether it is day-to-day stress or a major life stress. It is not so much the stress itself that creates our distress, it is the way we perceive and deal with it.

The way we perceive our anxiety disorder is a classic example. We perceive it to be a life-threatening event or a threat to our sanity or feelings of control. In reality we have an anxiety disorder. We don't die or go insane or lose control as a result of it. How we feel when we have a panic attack or feel anxious is how we are supposed to feel when we have them! Because we don't see the reality of our experience, we add further stress in the way we deal with it by being anxious and panicking about our anxiety and attacks.

Even when we do accept that we are indeed experiencing an anxiety disorder, we place unrealistic expectations and demands on our self. A workshop participant was very upset during a workshop. He said to me:

I should never have had this panic attack. It should never have happened. I am not scared of the shopping centre so it shouldn't have happened. I can't believe that I have let myself down like this.

Why 'shouldn't' it have happened? How did he let himself down? He had panic disorder. This means he will have an attack on occasions. This is the reality of his situation. Yet he was not accepting the reality and, by not doing so, he added additional stress and anxiety.

When we reach our threshold to stress, the additional stress of our attacks and anxiety can mean that our threshold to stress can spiral down. As Vicki said to Karen, we can start to 'run on empty'. Some people reach the point where they can't tolerate any stress at all. They have zero tolerance to stress and their anxiety levels are at the top of the scale at number ten. Recovery means bringing our threshold to stress up to a higher level and reducing our anxiety level to zero.

From: Martha

SUBJECT: REBUILDING

This thought came to mind. In some ways we are dismantling and rebuilding ourselves. It reminds me in some way of my current living situation. We are remodelling our entire house. It is still the same house, the foundation is still intact, but new things are being added or replaced and it is messy and inconvenient. The same with rebuilding ourselves. It is messy and very uncomfortable at times.

Working through to recovery

* How would you rate your threshold to stress?
* How would you rate your overall anxiety levels?
* What issues do you need to address during the recovery process?
  – avoidance behaviour;
  – prescribed-drug addiction;
  – alcohol dependency;
  – current personal issues;
  – past personal issues;
  – any childhood abuse issues.

How did you rate your threshold to stress? How did you rate your overall levels of anxiety? By meditating every day and by developing our mindfulness skills we reduce our anxiety levels and build back our tolerance to stress.

For example, if we have zero tolerance to stress, we meditate and begin to work to control our panic and anxiety thinking by being aware and not becoming attached to our thoughts. Our threshold to stress begins to rise and our anxiety begins to diminish. When we reach 'level one' a 'window' opens. All anxiety, panic and fear disappears and is replaced with feelings of clarity and freedom. We then perceive and understand our disorder in an entirely different way. We see very clearly how it is all being created, and we see why there is no reason to fear it.

The feelings of clarity and freedom represent the integration of our emotional understanding and our intellectual understanding. However, as our threshold to stress is still very low, the 'window' closes as soon as we meet a stress that is higher than we can tolerate. And this does not take very long to happen! Especially at the lower levels, the window can close within an hour. When this happens, we immediately lose the intellectual/ emotional connection and we become caught up again in the panic and anxiety cycle. This is the first setback.

Setbacks

I know this is not what you wanted to hear! But setbacks are part of the working-through process. If we are prepared to work with them, they can become our greatest teacher because they can teach us so much about our disorder and about ourselves.

Some people comment that the word 'setback' is negative but, realistically, in the beginning they do set us back. As the process of recovery gains momentum, we change our perception of them and see them for what they are — another learning curve on the road to recovery.

When we have a setback, we need to extend our mindfulness skills. We need to become aware of why the 'window' has closed. At the lower stress threshold levels, it could be any number of reasons.

We may not have been aware that we momentarily dissociated and became caught up in our thoughts about it. Or a car back-firing or a dog barking could have startled us. We could be thinking about how great we feel and wouldn't it be awful if the anxiety comes back, which it usually does as soon as we have that thought!

When we identify the stress, we need to begin to deal with it as it is. Not how we think it, or we, should be. We then need to continue to meditate and practise our mindfulness skills. Our threshold to stress will continue to rise and the window will open again, this time at level two. Any stress higher than level two will close the window again. We repeat the process outlined above. This is the working-through process.

From: Karen
SUBJECT: HELP!

I think of a setback as a recurrence of strong physical symptoms, such as dizziness and shakiness. That's what I've been experiencing lately, stronger physical sensations. Thought-wise I seem to be doing okay, but it seems as if my body has a mind of its own. I know it doesn't, but it seems that way.

Funny thing is I'm not really panicking. It's just a very high anxiety, shaky, dizzy. I don't fear panic at all. I don't fear anxiety, either. I'm just at my limit with feeling anxious. I'm sick of it already. Okay, so I did great today, I visited my friend, but I was so anxious and shaky and didn't stay long.

When will I ever be able to just do things without anxiety? I think I get upset that I am dealing with panic disorder, and doing the exposure work brings up the fact that I have agoraphobia. It takes me out of my denial and upsets me.

Could this be a reaction to my risk taking? What do I think when I take these risks? Let's see. 'I can't believe I have to go through this. Why did this have to happen to me? Why can't I be like everybody else? Will I ever be able to feel normal again, lead a normal life? I've missed so much in life. When will I finally recover? I'm tired of this!' Gee, I guess I'm still locked into some pretty negative thinking. But when I wake up in the morning and the anxiety is still there, I get very discouraged.

For the life of me I can't figure out what that missing piece is. Trying to force recovery? I just want to feel relaxed and normal again. The lingering anxiety is a stubborn old cow that doesn't seem to want to budge. Maybe I should just resign myself to feeling this way, and do my best to live with it? What more can I do? I'm working with my thoughts.

I think I should just work on accepting this last part of the anxiety, because trying to make it go away isn't working. I've even found myself considering medication, which I've been committed to *not* doing all this time. I'm starting to worry that this last part of the anxiety is chemical and that I can't do anything about it, no matter how much I work with my thoughts.

I've been stuck at this point for at least a month or two. Maybe more. That's what's worrying and scaring me. I don't like the idea that there is nothing I can do about this anxiety, except take something, and I don't want to take anything.

Does this sound familiar? We do get trapped and we do go round and round, trying to break through and it can seem so overwhelming. Let's work through Karen's email to see how we can break the impasse.

Karen   I think of a setback as a recurrence of strong physical symptoms, such as dizziness and shakiness. That's what I've been experiencing lately, stronger physical sensations. Thought-wise I seem to be doing okay, but it seems as if my physical body has a mind of its own. I know it doesn't, but it seems that way.

Bronwyn *Thought-wise, no, you are not doing okay. You would not be having symptoms if your thoughts were on the right track.*

Karen   Funny thing is I'm not really panicking. It's just a very high anxiety, shaky, dizzy. I don't fear panic at all. I don't fear anxiety, either. I'm just at my limit with feeling anxious. I'm sick of it already.

Bronwyn *You are fighting it, Karen. It is a matter of simply letting it be there. So what if you're anxious? Don't buy into it. As Vicki said, you are adding a lot of unhelpful thoughts.*

Karen   Okay, so I did great today, I visited my friend, but I was so anxious and shaky and didn't stay long!

Bronwyn *Check and see. I think you were anxious when you were with her because you didn't know 'how to be' anymore. What mask to wear, so to speak. As I always say, become aware of what your anxiety is trying to tell you, teach you.*

Karen   When will I ever be able to just do things without anxiety??

Bronwyn *Don't you think this is going to make you anxious?*

Karen   I think I get upset that I am dealing with panic disorder and doing the exposure work brings up the fact that I have agoraphobia. It takes me out of my denial and upsets me.

Bronwyn *So when are you going to accept it? Denial equals anxiety because you are invalidating yourself.*

Karen Could this be a reaction to my risk taking?

Bronwyn *Vicki is totally right when she says, 'Not necessarily. I think it's a reaction to what you think about when you have taken these risks. Not the risk taking in itself.'*

Karen What do I think when I take these risks? Let's see. 'I can't believe I have to go through this. Why did this have to happen to me? Why can't I be like everybody else? Will I ever be able to feel normal again, lead a normal life? I've missed so much in life. When will I finally be recovered! I'm tired of this!' Gee, I guess I'm still locked into some pretty negative thinking.

Bronwyn *All of this equals anxiety.*

Karen But when I wake up in the morning and the anxiety is still there, I get very discouraged.

Bronwyn *Because you are looking for it. The radar is turned on.*

Karen For the life of me I can't figure out what that missing piece is.

Bronwyn *The way you are thinking.*

Karen Trying to force recovery?

Bronwyn *You are. You are fighting every step of the way. In the wrong way.*

Karen I just want to feel relaxed and normal again.

Bronwyn *Relax into it, Karen. Let yourself be anxious. As I say in the book, let it be there. You don't need to get involved with it.*

Karen   The lingering anxiety is a stubborn old cow that doesn't seem to want to budge.

Bronwyn   *It won't budge because you won't stop thinking about it.*

Karen   Maybe I should just resign myself to feeling this way, and do my best to live with it? What more can I do? I'm working with my thoughts.

Bronwyn   *Karen. Good grief! You are working with your thoughts, but you are still buying into the whole thing. Stop fighting it! Let it be there and let go of all the thoughts you have about it.*

Karen   I think I should just work on accepting this last part of the anxiety, because trying to make it go away isn't working.

Bronwyn   *Of course it won't. It won't go away until you let it be there and work with your thoughts that are creating it.*

Karen   I've even found myself considering medication, which I've been committed to *not* doing all this time. I'm starting to worry that this last part of the anxiety is chemical and that I can't do anything about it, no matter how much I work with my thoughts.

Bronwyn   *As I said, you are fighting it. Fight equals the fight-or-flight response.*

Karen   I've been stuck at this point for at least a month or two. Maybe more. That's what's worrying and scaring me.

Bronwyn   *And that isn't making you anxious? Look at what has happened in the last month or more. You have fought your emotions, fought your feelings. Don't you think that in itself will make you anxious?*

Karen   I don't like the idea that there is nothing I can do about this anxiety, except take something, and I don't want to take anything.

Bronwyn   *And this isn't making you anxious?*

From: Karen

SUBJECT: HELP

Bronwyn, you must be ready to fly all the way to the USA and slap me silly! LOL. You and Vicki are 100% right. Hate you both. I am still fighting it. I want to be *recovered already*! Arggghhhh!!! And every time I feel anxious or emotional, I get upset that I'm *not recovered already*!! I'm being impatient. I want to skip the exposure work, skip the emotional breakthroughs, and advance directly into full happy joyous recovery. I don't want to pass 'go' or collect two hundred dollars! I want to go to recovery, directly to recovery!!!!!

On top of that I'm adding tons of fear thoughts. Not that I fear the panic or the anxiety, but I fear the idea of never recovering, and that's what's keeping me anxious. I fear admitting fully the extent of my problem.

I think it's time to wave the white flag of surrender here, and surrender to the fact that, yes, I *do* have agoraphobia and anxiety. Yes, my life *has* been limited. Yes, now I do have to do this exposure work and yes it does stink. It is hard, tiring and upsetting. And yes! I do feel like crying for many reasons. And yes I do still feel anxious and might feel it for a while yet, as I'm working through all this. I give up! Uncle! Uncle! Now back into the lab, Igor. Not to build a monster, but to take one apart. One thought at a time. Don't worry if I don't surface for a while. This may take some time.

The second layer

As I said in the first chapter, the recovery process is like peeling an onion. When we first begin to work on our recovery we work with the top layer. And these are our obvious loud, attention-getting, panic anxiety thoughts and fears. As we become more mindful, we see the next layer of thoughts that also create our anxiety and panic.

From: Bronwyn

SUBJECT: THRESHOLD TO STRESS

What Vicki meant about identifying the sources of stress in our life is not just becoming aware of how we deal with major stress, but how we deal with day-to-day stress, including those situations where we unknowingly create unnecessary stress.

One of the classic ways we create this unnecessary stress is by thinking 'What will people think?'

What happens if you hear a knock on the door? What do you think when you hear the knock? 'Oh no, I don't want anyone here. I haven't made the beds, vacuumed the house, washed the walls and curtains, cleaned the windows, done the dishes and steam-cleaned every thing else, since last night. I haven't any make-up on. My hair is a mess. What are they going to think? Oh no, here comes the anxiety. I can't breathe. What am I going to do now?'

We immediately generate anxiety by the way we are thinking. In reality, all that has happened is someone has knocked at the door! We need to see how we can trigger our anxiety by the way we think about even the most ordinary everyday situations. We need to learn to deal with these situations the way they really are. Our mental health needs to be more important than what other people think of us.

'Someone is at the door. The house is untidy. Okay. So the house isn't going to be a feature in a 'beautiful homes of the year' magazine, and I have no make-up on and my hair is a mess. They will just have to get over it. I will see what they want. If I don't want them to stay, I will tell them I am having a bad hair day and can they come back at a time that's suitable for both of us.'

Another classic is how we take responsibility for other people's problems. How many hours have we spent on the phone, allowing people to download all their problems onto us? And they usually always ring at dinner time. Have you noticed that? How many hours have we spent giving the most excellent advice, while our dinner goes cold?

If that isn't enough, how do we feel once we get off the phone? 'Poor Jane, she has so many problems. I feel so bad for her. I am so worried about her. There has to be something more I can do for her. What if that happened to me. What would I do? Oh no, what if that does happen to me? *What if it did?* I can't think about it. I have to stop thinking about it. But what if it *did?* Why is my heart racing? Oh no. What's my pulse? Oh, it is so high!'

Then a week later Jane rings back at her normal time, your dinner time, and downloads the same problems as last week. But this time with the added bonus of the latest weekly update, which adds another thirty minutes to the phone call. And of course she hasn't taken any of the advice you have given her over the last few weeks. There are always numerous reasons why she hasn't, and they all sound very legitimate. All the same, she asks you what she can do, and pleads with you to help her.

What do you think? 'Why does she always ring me? Doesn't she feed her family? Why can't she work it out herself? I am so sick of this. Oh no, I can't breathe, I feel dizzy, here it comes again.'

A far less stressful and more compassionate approach for both of you would be, 'Jane, I'm serving dinner, so I'm not able to spend time with you at the moment. I realise you're distressed, but we have discussed this a number of times. What can you do to help yourself in this situation? Can you think about this? See what you can do and who you can contact for assistance. I need to get back to dinner now.'

But we can also let this become yet another stressful situation: 'What will she think of me? Why did I do that? She needs help. Why was I so selfish? Oh no, my heart is racing, I feel shaky, I have to get dinner. I feel too sick to eat?'

We need to see how our need to be all things to all people plays a significant role in creating unnecessary stress, and how this can induce setbacks. This also applies to the major stresses that happen to all of us during our life. We deal with these stresses, again by trying to be all things to all people. Working through major life stresses means we need to be able to deal with these stresses as they are, not how we think we 'should' react. This is part of learning to become our real self and I discuss this in the following chapters.

When we have a setback, we need to become aware of:

- the immediate stress;
- how we thought about it;
- how we reacted to it;
- how we dealt with it;
- whether we dealt with it in a realistic way;
- whether we dealt with it from our expectations and demands of how we should be;
- whether we are meditating;
- whether we are developing our mindfulness skills.

From: Vicki

SUBJECT: BAD DAY

It's realistic to expect to have days when you feel great, like you have done on those days when you were doing well. Go for this, Karen. Just now, you're working through some things that won't hang around for ever. It's realistic to expect off days. See them as such. As to what is happening for you now . . .

Karen   I'm beginning to see that I view morning anxiety as defeat, as evidence that no matter how much progress I make during the previous day, no matter where I go or what I accomplish, if I wake up with morning anxiety it means I am not recovering.

Vicki   *There is no need to look any further, Karen, for the reason your anxiety is ongoing. While accepting that there are good reasons for the way you feel, and not beating yourself up for thinking you have got it 'wrong', you can work on the things that cause your daily anxiety, not the anxiety itself as such.*

Karen   I've been doing so many great things, going places I'd never have gone before, doing things I never did before. But I find that I'm telling myself, 'What good is doing all these great things if I only feel crappy anyway?'

Vicki   *Because, Karen, the crappy feeling doesn't last. I felt this myself, dragging myself through things, wondering, 'What the hell am I doing this for? It's not that much fun.' But you are subtly working away, doing some real good work. I too was impatiently wanting the feeling of anxiety to go forever. And it does!*

I realised that accepting our anxiety comes as 'natural' to us as accepting the feelings during full panic. Not very naturally at all! It's natural for us to want to fight it. But let go of the need to stop the anxiety, just as you let the feelings of panic go. Stick with it, Karen, you have learnt so much, I have no doubt you will break through here too!

From: Karen

SUBJECT: BAD DAY

Vicki, you are right in what you say. How I felt yesterday is a clue on how I can expect to feel as I recover. This hit a nerve with me, which is easy to do these days with so many of them exposed! I have had some really great days. Days that I was anxiety free, panic free. Just feeling happy and great, as if I can take on the world.

Unfortunately, days like this haven't been too many, but what you're saying is that these types of days are what we can look forward to when we have recovered. It really gives me something to keep working towards.

I think one of the things getting in my way is the fear that how I feel now is just about as good as it's going to get. That I'm always going to have this higher than average level of anxiety, that I'll always be so preoccupied with my health, always having to psyche myself up to go into the store and then have to deal with symptoms while in the store. Basically, that I'll never be 'like anyone else'.

Your comment helped me to realise that recovery takes time and I will feel wonderful and free and clear when I am recovered. I suppose I'm just afraid I'll never reach my destination. Thanks for the reminder. I'll use those great days as an incentive to keep me going.

While we can be committed to recovery 'no matter what the cost' we do need to learn patience. And then more patience! With ourselves and the overall recovery process. We need to remember, we are 'dismantling' sometimes years of associations and conditioning, as a result of our anxiety disorder. We are also 'dismantling' a lifetime of being all things to all people. This is going to take time. And taking this time is necessary. It enables us to rebuild our lives on surer footings.

Avoidance behaviour: working on it

Part of the process of recovery means working on our avoidance behaviour. Many people think they need to approach their avoidance behaviour in a non-anxiety, non-panic state. It doesn't work like this. We need to be anxious, and a panic attack or two while working on our avoidance behaviour, would also be of benefit! Recovery means that we can be in any situation or place, and if we become anxious, or have an attack, we can control it then and there, without needing to leave and without even thinking we need to leave.

Most of us use a graded exposure technique when working on our avoidance behaviour. This means, as the name suggests, gradually exposing ourselves to the situations and places we have been avoiding. Although people find these techniques frightening, they are not as demanding as a 'flooding' technique. 'Flooding' techniques involve exposing ourselves immediately to our most feared situations, and these techniques can be counterproductive for some people.

When we first begin to do work on our avoidance behaviour using a graded exposure method, we need to remember that our mindfulness skills are usually very rudimentary and that it can be difficult for us to achieve all we want to achieve in that particular session. Some graded exposure programs ask that people stay in the situation or place until their panic and anxiety levels subside. In the early stages of recovery, this can be very difficult.

While our attack will subside in time, our anxiety can remain high because we are attached to our thoughts of, 'I can't do this. My anxiety is too high. What can I do? I feel terrible? Why hasn't the anxiety gone away? I hate this. What is wrong with me? Why can't I do this? I am such a failure, I am so weak. I should be able to do this.'

All these thoughts do is keep our anxiety going. Sometimes it is of greater benefit to simply go home, rather than fighting to stay and fighting to get our anxiety down. Fighting it will only keep it going!

Going home is not defeat. It is not failure, so long as we go back out the next day and attempt it again. When we get home we can review where we became caught up. We can track back and see where and how we attached into our thoughts and how this created our anxiety and perhaps panic. Doing a review like this will teach us where we need to be more mindful, where we need to become the umpire in the game and not its reluctant player.

We can then 'begin again'. These two words can give us the freedom to let go of the times when our graded exposure program, or our practice of mindfulness, did not work out the way we would have liked. All we need do is review where we can improve and then begin again. And we will be 'beginning again' quite a bit during the recovery process!

We also need to make allowances in working with a graded exposure program. We need the freedom to be able to do what feels right for us. And that does not necessarily mean, 'I am out of here!' It means making allowances for our self.

We need to be able to set our own exposure program and we need to be able to have control of it. In some cases our program is set by other people and we follow along doing what we think we should do. We feel the pressure to 'perform' as perfectly as possible. This, of course, begins another mind game called 'perfect recovery'. All this does is make us resistant to doing the program. We need a choice, and we need the flexibility to be able to choose what we want to do at any point in the program. If we know we have a choice, we become the umpire, not a player.

If we want a mobile phone with us when practising, then we carry one. If we know we can call for assistance at any time, this eases the pressure. If we need to sit behind a potted palm when we first visit a restaurant again, then we sit behind the potted palm. If we need to sit in an aisle seat next to the exit in the theatre or cinema then we sit in an aisle seat next to the exit. If we need the security of a tranquilliser in our wallet then we need the security of a tranquilliser in our wallet. When we can approach our exposure work in a more relaxed way, we will be able to accomplish so much more than if we have a list of 'shoulds' and 'should nots' in our pocket.

From: Angie

SUBJECT: WORKING IT

I find that if I just go ahead, and do what I want to do, always remembering to use the techniques in *Power over Panic*, the actual doing is not nearly as fearful as the anticipation. Sometimes it is hard, but the more I do this, remembering that I am not going to lose control, I am not going to die if I have a panic attack, the easier it becomes.

I needed to go grocery shopping this morning, and I was starting to feel the fear coming up as I was getting ready to go. I went out the door, and it was almost like a relief to actually do it, instead of dreading it. I felt the fresh air on my face and I got this wonderful feeling of freedom.

I still was a little fearful, but I am finding more and more that the fear is not as bad as the staying home and being angry because I didn't go. This takes time and a lot of patience. I have been practising the techniques for about three months. You will also get there. Just be gentle and patient with yourself.

We do need to be mindful of our anticipatory anxiety. We can set ourselves up for further anxiety and panic, hours or days, before we do any graded exposure work. We need to be mindful and work with these thoughts before we leave home! It can save us additional panic and anxiety while we are working on our exposure program.

From: Karen
SUBJECT: RESISTANCE

I am this close to calling up and postponing the placement test at the university. Which is my pattern. Ooooooooooh, I am so #$% angry I could jump up and down and tear my hair out. I do not want my life to be one big struggle just to do normal everyday things. Will I always feel this when I am doing new things? What is the best way through this phase of recovery?

From: Bronwyn
SUBJECT: RESISTANCE

Well, don't pull your hair out, because then you will be worried about what people will think because you are bald.

What you need to do is stop struggling with it. This is the hardest part. You need to go out, and do all the things you need and want to do. Use your anger to get you out there. Use it against the panic and anxiety.

When you begin to do new things, remember you probably will feel anxious and perhaps panic. But this is where you need to separate out 'growth' anxiety from anxiety disorder anxiety. They can feel the same, but they are different. Growth anxiety is healthy, normal and natural. You will feel this when you take on a new challenge, like doing the placement test. Most people do. This also applies to feelings of excitement. These can also feel like anxiety disorder anxiety. Part of recovery means learning to tell the difference and not attach to our thoughts about them. Let us know how you go.

From: Karen
SUBJECT: I DID IT!!!

I did it!! I finally did it!!! I went to the university today and took the placement test. It went for two-and-a-half hours. There were other people in the room also taking the test. All of us were sitting at a big round table facing each other (yikes!). I didn't panic at all, didn't even come close. I felt a tiny bit anxious but I think it was normal anxiety. I didn't feel trapped. I didn't feel the need to get out of there. Didn't worry about how long it was going to take. Didn't worry about panicking.

I did it. I did it. I did it!!! I told my panic disorder I don't care what it's was saying, what it was telling me to do. I was going to take that dammed test and I didn't care what the disorder had to say about it. Then I marched in there and did it.

I left the building feeling like I was walking on air. When I got in my car I cried out 'Wooooooooooo Hoooooooooo!' *I did it!!!!* And I don't care if anyone saw me. This one accomplishment has made all my doubts seem weak. I can feel them shrivelling up and dying off. I can almost feel my panic disorder melting away like the wicked witch of the west after Dorothy doused her!! Keep at it everybody. It works, it works. It works!!!!

The more mindful we become, the more we work with our thoughts, the easier it becomes to break through our avoidance behaviour. And the more we work it, the more our perception of our attacks and anxiety changes. Once this happens, it becomes even easier to work through to recovery.

From: Karen
SUBJECT: PERCEPTION CHANGE
Yesterday was my 'first day out' testing my new attitude, my new perception of things. I went to the supermarket first. Well, I sat in the parking lot and said, 'I hope I go in there and panic like crazy! I need some practice!' Then I took a sip of water and off I went.

The dairy section is all the way at the back of the store and to the right.   All the way I kept saying to myself, 'Well, go ahead and panic already! Don't you feel anxious? Gee, doesn't everything look creepy in here? No? What do you mean no?! Sure it does. Hey, don't you feel dizzy yet? Look up at the ceiling, woooooo, so high. Feel spacey? Go *ahead! Panic!!*'

Nothing happened. I felt fine. I got the milk without a hitch, and even stood on a regular line instead of the express line! While in line I did the same thing. 'Now's your chance to get some real good practice. Let's go! Panic girl!! Panic, panic, panic!!!' Nothing again.

Have you ever tried to have an attack. Have you ever tried to deliberately make yourself anxious, make yourself panic? Try and see what happens!

Medication

Part of our recovery may mean a gradual withdrawal from our medication, including tranquillisers or antidepressants. As I've said before, it is important that we don't just stop taking our medication. We need to do this under medical supervision. Our doctor will prepare a reduction plan for us which we do need to follow. If we do find that we experience withdrawal symptoms from tranquillisers, or discontinuation symptoms from antidepressants, then it is important that we discuss this with our doctor.

During this phase of my own recovery, I found that my daily practice of meditation and my mindfulness skills enabled me to work through my withdrawal symptoms in the same way as I had with my attacks and anxiety. I let the withdrawal symptoms happen and did not become involved with my anxious thoughts about them!

Alcohol dependence

If we do have a dependency on alcohol, we need to address this as part of recovery. Organisations such as Alcoholics Anonymous can be of assistance and benefit, and can provide the support we need. Again our panic anxiety management skills can be utilised during this period.

> **From: Karen**
> **SUBJECT: GETTING THERE**
> Another successful day out. Not successful because I felt perfectly relaxed, because I didn't, but successful because I felt anxious and didn't buy into it.

Use this checklist when you are having a setback to help you isolate the reasons why it has happened and what you can do to assist yourself with working through it.

Setback checklist

- [ ] Are you learning to be kind to yourself?
- [ ] Do you accept your diagnosis of an anxiety disorder?
- [ ] Do you accept you have an anxiety disorder?
- [ ] Are you being completely honest with your doctor?
- [ ] Are you asking for assistance when you need it?
- [ ] If you are using medication, are you following the guidelines prescribed by your doctor?
- [ ] Do you blame or mentally abuse yourself because you have an anxiety disorder or because you have had a setback?
- [ ] Is your recovery your number one priority?
- [ ] Do you ensure you are taking at least twenty minutes a day to meditate or use another relaxation technique?
- [ ] Are you developing mindfulness skills?
- [ ] Are you committed and disciplined in practising this daily or only on occasions when you think about it?
- [ ] Are you facing situations and places that you have avoided while you develop mindfulness skills?
- [ ] Can you identify the stress which created the setback?
- [ ] How did you think about it?
- [ ] How did you react to it?
- [ ] How did you deal with it?
- [ ] Did you deal with it in a realistic way?
- [ ] Did you deal with it from your expectations and demands of how you should be?

From: Karen

SUBJECT: LEARNING

You are so close to recovery, I'd hate to see you give up now. I feel the same way a lot of times. I'm almost afraid to trust the fact that I've made so much progress, afraid that if I push the limit a little too far, I will relapse. Or afraid to really consider myself recovered. I suppose part of it is that I don't want to be taken off guard, I don't want the rug pulled out from under me, the way it was when this disorder really hit me.

Yesterday, I found myself really feeling discouraged, feeling as if I have not made an ounce of progress since day one. Then I said to myself, 'Okay, let's see if I can find some things I have made progress with, things that *have* changed.' And sure enough there were many, many ways I have changed, many things I have made progress in. While I'm not 100% anxiety free, and I still have avoidances to overcome, and self-esteem issues to work out, I have made tremendous progress in the fact that:

1. I no longer fear panic and anxiety.
2. I have taken risks and have done fine, and not so fine too, but I took risks!
3. I'm beginning to see myself in a new way.
4. I'm now aware of my self-esteem issues and my anxiety.
5. I'm losing fear of my emotions, beginning to let myself feel again, and express those feelings.

I think you can say the same things about yourself, too. A lot of the fear is gone, yet some still remains, mostly fear of setbacks. I think it's because we have tasted the freedom, and the thought of losing it becomes more unbearable.

The way I've been working on this is:

I tell myself that I have sure been through the worst I could ever imagine, and I'm still here. I'm alive, I'm sane, I'm making progress. In other words, I *handled* it, and I have overcome a lot of it. A relapse would be very upsetting. I'd probably just want to lay down and cover my head for a month!

But, even if it did happen, I would handle it the same way I handled all the rest. I did it once, I would be able to do it again. It would not be pleasant, but I have the power within me to deal with it.

I think the closer we get to recovery, the fear shifts. First the fear was of the symptoms and the panic. We feared we were sick, going crazy, losing control. Later, when we're close to freedom, we fear losing that freedom, losing all the progress we've made. We need to learn that just like the panic was harmless, our fear of losing freedom is also harmless. It's just a thought.

We also need to remind ourselves where this disorder gets its power. From *us*. From our fear, our worry, our dwelling on it. A few days ago, I wrote to the group worrying that I was becoming more agoraphobic, that 'it' was getting worse. Vicki reminded me that it's still just thoughts! I didn't have to work on 'agoraphobia', I had to work on the thoughts. It's easy to slip back into focusing on the symptoms, we're so good at it! It's the thoughts we need to keep working on.

And Karen is correct. It is our thoughts we need to keep working with. As people begin to recover, they do 'look over their shoulder', waiting and wondering if the panic and anxiety is going to return. Or afraid that the 'big one' is suddenly going to appear and take them by surprise.

Recovery is the loss of fear of our attacks and our anxiety. Our disorder, as Karen says, gets its power from us. From our thoughts! The more mindful we become, the more we take back the power and we choose not to become caught up again.

> **From: Lorrie**
> **SUBJECT: CHOICE**
> Yes, Yes, Yes!!! Isn't it such a relief when you finally realise that this whole thing is a CHOICE???!! . . . It's like all of a sudden you give yourself permission to just 'be' . . . No more fighting it, but instead choosing not to get involved in it.

CHAPTER 10

HANDY HINTS

From: Karen

SUBJECT: ANXIETY RATING

I used to monitor my anxiety levels every day in my journal. I'd describe how the day went, how I was feeling and then rate my anxiety for the day on a scale from one to ten. I did this mainly to track my progress, or lack of progress. I really didn't see that by doing this, I was focusing in on 'how I felt' again, which naturally makes you more aware of your anxiety.

I decided I wouldn't rate my anxiety level for a while, so I stopped doing it. Well, I never started up again, and I'm not sure if it's a coincidence or not, but my anxiety levels have been much much lower, and even my morning anxiety is almost undetectable.

I think self-awareness can go a little off track and turn into something detrimental instead of helpful. Monitoring our negative thoughts and behaviours is helpful, we can't recover if we don't do this. But monitoring our level of anxiety to measure our progress, or as a way of keeping 'watch' on things so it doesn't come back, is dwelling on it too much. Doing this we become more aware of our anxiety instead of less aware of it.

I know we need to be aware of our anxiety, so we can work with it. But I think the monitoring we do is more a fearful watchfulness. Keeping one eye on the door in case the bogey tries to get back in. That kind of monitoring causes more anxiety. I find the more I work on letting myself be, letting go of things, the better I feel.

From: Lorrie
SUBJECT: CHOICE

It has taken me years to learn that *it is a choice* in how I deal with or react to my attacks and anxiety. It never felt like there was a choice, because the fear just came too fast to feel like I had that choice. But with practice and *truly believing* that I am in no danger from an attack or even panic, and they are two different things at that moment, I can finally see that the choice is mine and always will be.

But, I think the important thing I learnt is that I expect I will always have occasional attacks throughout my life. I am built this way mentally and physically. I will, of course, continue to work on the stressful ways I conduct my life, that make me more prone to them, but I will not always panic. *That choice is mine!!!*

From: Karen
SUBJECT: CHOICE

Thanks, Lorrie! For the past two days I have been feeling dizzy, and yesterday I felt so weak and 'off' I felt like I would nearly collapse. The more I dwelled on how I felt, the more aware I became of how tired and weak I was feeling.

Then started the thoughts of 'why'? Why am I so tired? Why am I so weak? What's going on here? Maybe I'm sick? All this led to several tiny attacks, and a general underlying feeling of inner shakiness. I went to bed last night armed with *Power over Panic*, and a few tapes to get my head straight. I woke up feeling better this morning, but a bit on alert to see how I feel. Your email really woke me up to the idea that *yes*, I can feel anxious and have an attack. *So what!!! Yes!!*

It's been a stressful week or two and maybe I *need* an attack. But I don't have to panic about it. Nothing has 'returned'. I'm not relapsing or crazy or whatever else I can dream up. I just need to take some time to decompress, catch up on some rest, and pay attention to the thoughts I'm having that might be causing me to feel a bit more anxious. Thanks for the booster in the arm!! I needed it.

From: Martha
SUBJECT: CONSTANT ANXIETY

Two years ago I had constant anxiety. It was horrible. I look back on it now and I can see what I could have done. There has to be some sort of 'down time'. In other words, there needs to be time in the day for you to completely shut the thoughts down. Have you been doing the meditation? I am just learning how to meditate and it is helping me to let the thoughts drift in and out during the day.

I also learnt to take life in five minute increments. Sounds sort of silly, I know, but that gets me through those periods of high anxiety. I am learning not to wake up and flood myself with the day that is ahead of me. I am learning to take it as it comes, in five minute increments, if that's what it takes.

From: Melony
SUBJECT: DENTIST

I went to the dentist this morning. He said, 'Something dreadful must have happened for you to be here.' He really loves me! Anyway I had only a minimum of anxiety. I would call it a normal anxiety level for the dentist. He gave me an injection and filled the tooth and I was very proud of myself! Like you suggested, Vicki, I decided not to worry about it until it was too late to worry about it! Before, I would make myself feel sick thinking of all that he would have to do, but this time, the first time in my life, I thought, 'Okay, I have to have the tooth fixed, so be it!!'

From: Karen
SUBJECT: DISCOUNTING OURSELVES

I have taken an active role in recovery, but I think part of me is still hoping, wanting the 'cure' to come from an outside source. This made me realise I was approaching therapy as a weekly dose of 'medicine' that would help me recover. I was almost being dependent upon it. And while it has helped greatly, I'm still the one doing the work, it's still my problem, and only my effort is going to lead to recovery. At first this pissed me off a little, but then it made me realise something else.

With all the effort and hard work I've been putting in, I would never have guessed I was still being so passive in my approach. I've been seeing anxiety as something that has a grip on me and I'm trying to pry it loose, something *outside* of myself that has become attached to me. Now I realise that anxiety is coming from within, and the cure will come from within also.

I have been waking up in the morning with anxiety, as usual, and having an attitude of 'Oh no, it's still here. I hope this is a good day. Ugh! What if it's a bad day? When will this anxiety go away already!!' Hmmmm. Sounds a bit passive, don't you think?

And as far as how long it's going to take, I guess I'm just going to think of it like bodybuilding. Those guys don't build their muscles overnight. It takes daily work, lots of practice, commitment, time, and slowly their muscles build in strength and size.

Well, we're all working on getting stronger too, and it's going to take time before we look like Arnold Schwarzenegger!! But, oh boy! Won't the results be worth it?! Every time I catch myself thinking, 'What if I don't recover? What if I get worse?', I'm going to tell myself, 'Of course you're going to recover! People can change, they can retrain themselves. You have the power. You will make it happen.'

It doesn't matter what other people say or think about recovery, whether or not it's possible. I'm going to succeed. And it doesn't matter how long it takes. I think I was pressuring myself to hurry up and recover. But recovery is in *my* hands. Eureka!! It's not going to happen at the therapist's office, it happens every single day, moment to moment, with each and every passing thought. *That's* where recovery lies.

WOW!!! What a new sense of power and control this realisation has given me!! Approaching my recovery this way, from a more active than passive standpoint, has really lifted my spirits. Just realising that it was *me* all along who has gotten this far was a wonderful discovery. I think it's the sense of power I have over the anxiety, instead of feeling it has a power over me.

From: Bronwyn
SUBJECT: DISCOUNTING OURSELVES

Yes, Karen. Yes!! This is actually a big breakthrough. I say this because everyone discounts themselves during the recovery process. It is the half-full, half-empty glass scenario. People say to me that they are not making any progress, that their exposure program is not going well, and overall they really think they are not recovering. Yet, when I ask them how they are going with mindfulness, they will tell me they are able to see their thoughts and they are becoming skilled in controlling them. They will tell me they are learning to let their attacks happen, and they are seeing how quickly they disappear. And they will tell me how they are now able to drive again, or how they are able to travel further than they were before. But they don't see this. They discount it totally and call it all a 'fluke', and then hook into the times they felt anxious or panicked or had an attack.

They simply don't realise that they *are* 'working it' and are actually recovering. This is why I always say, people won't see how far they have come until they have almost recovered, because they just don't see it as it is!

From: Karen, Bronwyn and Jill

SUBJECT: DISSOCIATION

Karen   *I find I can actually think myself into dissociating. Does that sound possible?*

Bronwyn When this happens check whether you are staring at whatever you are looking at. Or how much are you going over things in your mind? Our self-absorption can also induce these states.

Karen   *Yes!! Sometimes I catch myself looking at something, or someone, and just waiting for it to look 'funny'. It's amazing how we can be so unaware of our own thoughts and behaviours.*

Jill   I have been really watching myself lately when I go into the dissociative state. I can literally feel myself going into it. The pictures that run through my mind when this happens are like a full-length movie! I am actually starting to enjoy it when I am tired at night. I know that sounds weird, but when I have no fear of it, I find it relaxing.

From: Lorrie

SUBJECT: DISTRACTIONS

I used to have 'temporary recoveries', then relapse. I could never figure out why that was until I realised that I was not using CBT, but more distraction techniques. Now, with continued practice of mindfulness, my old habitual thoughts just don't come the same way anymore and my new realistic thoughts are more the habit now.

I will be soon facing my tough times again, as I travel for six months of the year and travelling is my only issue now. I still find I am avoiding putting myself in the situations that are the hardest for me. For the first time though, I feel this underlying belief that I'm going to put myself out there and go for some of the things that I've been holding back. My fear is of the 'big one' and I know it is *not* going to happen, but I will never completely believe this until I get out there and prove it to myself. I'm at the point where I can't finish this last bit of this recovery, until I get out there and do the work.

From: Jill

SUBJECT: DRIVING

In regards to your driving I found what had helped me is to do this very gradually. I can drive all day if I am in my comfort zone and that can mean miles and miles. When I drive out of it, and I am practising doing this, I just take it one step at a time and if it's too hard that day I know I can just turn around and come back.

I remember one day I really wanted to go to a craft market and for me to go I would have to drive myself so I did. Along the way I was saying out loud, 'I am anxious' and the fear would disappear. Rather than fighting the fear, I just accepted it being there.

I have been to that market a few times since, some of the route I take is slightly longer. I do that at the moment because it just feels more comfortable and that's okay. Practise with what is comfortable for you and take it step by step.

From: Lorrie

SUBJECT: DRIVING

Yep, yep. Me too!! I'll be driving along and as soon as I get out of my 'comfort zone' all of a sudden I feel totally alone and isolated and start thinking about 'what ifs' all over the place. Finally, some time ago I had a total panic attack one day and, of course, immediately stopped and turned around and drove home. I don't even remember the whole drive home but I learnt one thing at least that day. I sure do have great homing instincts!!!

For some reason, even though that was a horrible experience and shook me up for days, I never feared that I would not be able to drive home again. It took sometime longer for me to learn that it wasn't necessary to turn around, because there just wasn't even a possibility of going insane or dying; like Bronwyn says 'it would have happened already'.

Here's my new motto that I live by, if you get sick of hearing it you have to blame Vicki. LOL. *There is no big one!!!!* You've already experienced the worst you ever will. You're not insane now and you never will be!!!

From: Bronwyn

SUBJECT: ENERGY LEVELS

It is important for us to maintain our energy levels. It is our responsibility to ensure we are eating properly and that we begin an exercise program to build back our overall fitness levels. Some people say to me that they are so exhausted they are unable to exercise. But when we do begin to exercise, even if it is a short walk, we will find that our energy levels increase, rather than decrease. Consider joining a gym and speaking to a fitness trainer. Not only would it be great practice as part of our overall graded exposure program, we can begin to feel much better physically. A two for one deal!

From: Bronwyn
SUBJECT: FAMILY

Not only are we affected by our disorder, so too is our family. This is not a reason to feel guilty! It isn't our fault that we have developed a disorder. Family members ask me what they can do to help their partner, son or daughter recover, and the first thing I say is take care of yourself first. This is just as important as making sure our recovery is our number one priority. We all need to take care of ourselves first. This way we can give more effective support to other people.

Although we may be restricted because of agoraphobia, it is also important that family members live their normal lives. I know this can be difficult, because some people with a disorder are unable to be alone. It is a matter of discussing and working out a solution that takes into consideration the needs of everyone concerned.

Partners and family members can be of great assistance (if we will let them) in helping us learn to develop our mindfulness skills. If we are having an attack or feeling anxious they can help us to see the thoughts that created it all. They can also assist us in working through our avoidance behaviour.

As we recover, we do begin to change. And as much as everyone wants us to recover, this can be frightening for partners and family members. It is so important that everyone discusses this. Not just on a superficial level, but in depth. We need to be able to talk about any fears we may have as a result of this process and so, too, do our partners and family members. They need to talk of any fears they may have as a result of the changes we are making. I can't emphasise enough how important this is. If we are able to be open and honest with each other, our relationships can strengthen and deepen. Communication is the key!

From: Bronwyn
SUBJECT: GOALS

I am not into setting goals. They can be so restrictive, because our need to be perfect means we need to reach our goals perfectly! And setting goals means we 'have to' reach them, no matter what. Which can mean we resist straight away!

I say to everyone: Just have one goal — recovery. This takes the pressure off in trying to meet 'goal one through to goal one hundred and one'. And it allows us the freedom to be spontaneous and creative during recovery.

The more aware we become the more we will feel our own intuition coming through. So many people say to me that they feel the intuition prompting them to go further into recovery, or to push past their limits of their avoidance behaviour, but they don't act on it. Why?? It's us teaching us, showing us how to recover.

If we can begin to act on our intuition at any point of the recovery process, it will enable us to move through to recovery more easily and more creatively.

This is why I say, don't set goals, because if we begin to follow our intuition we can go from say 'goal twenty-five to goal fifty-nine' in one swift move. Or we may realise that the goals we have set are too restrictive or unnecessary and so we can drop them altogether and change the direction of our recovery entirely. We need to listen to our self!

From: Karen and Vicki
SUBJECT: MORNING ANXIETY

Karen   I'm doing all the work, reading all the books, taking all the risks, catching all the thoughts, and still the anxiety is there. It makes me feel I just am not doing enough, or doing it right.

Vicki   *Give yourself some credit here for this. Beating yourself up for not making it work now is going to hold you back. You are laying some good solid foundations at the moment and when your 'inner self' trusts you enough not to pounce on it for every little error, it will relax and get to work with it, mistakes and all, as the war within you has stopped.*

Karen   Sometimes when I wake with morning anxiety my first thought is, 'Oh no, how am I ever going to get any work done today?' And if I don't/can't work, I feel horribly guilty, hence more anxiety. How can I begin to work on this?

Vicki   *By beginning to pull up the 'adult' in you and some responsible thinking. What thoughts can you think of here?*
'OK this comes and goes if I don't fight it.'
'I have felt worse than this and still done it.'
'I am still learning to work with this.'

Karen   Thanks for the encouragement. I will hold onto this thought for the rest of the weekend, and keep reassuring myself that this too shall pass.

Vicki   *All things do pass, keep noticing things like this.*

Karen   I'd take a good panic attack any day.

Vicki   *I've heard this many times!!!*

From: Melony
SUBJECT: MORNING ANXIETY
I have had a miserable week, mainly with morning anxiety. I get so sick and tired of this anxiety, like everyone else I guess. This morning I was feeling miserable as usual and trying to get a bit of enthusiasm to get ready for work! Could have easily crawled back into bed and faded away!! Anyway, I had typed out some emails from the group and read one, I think it was from Karen, that said in my words, 'Let the anxiety come and say to yourself, "this will give me something to practise with"! And I thought "right, I will give it a go" and, of course, you all know "it worked"!!'

From: Jill
SUBJECT: MOVING ON
I was getting myself quite down and depressed thinking I had wasted so much of my life through anxiety and fear, until I was telling my friend how I felt and she said, 'So, think what you can do with the rest of your life now.'

I feel like we have the opportunity now to just move on ahead in our own time when we are ready. I don't think we would have had an opportunity, and so much insight into what we can be, without having had this disorder. We have learnt so much about so many things.

The self issues are really hard sometimes to work with. I have been working through mine and they were very sad and confronting sometimes, but I feel I have been given a gift in some ways. I know that may sound strange, but as you slowly work through them (if you want to) it really can be the case and we get a real life back.

I am really finding some answers now, and they are as clear as day. They seem so simple when the penny drops. I didn't believe I could ever get over this anxiety, but each week something new just falls into place. Mind you I seem to have lived and breathed recovery for the last five months!

From: Bronwyn
SUBJECT: RECOVERY

The biggest mistake people make in working towards recovery is thinking that they will never have another panic attack. While, yes, people will recover to the degree they are working on it, the bottom line is we may still have an attack sometimes. Especially those of us who have had panic disorder. The dissociative ability doesn't go away, ability being the operative word. And it is those of us who dissociate who have the nocturnal attacks.

I have an attack occasionally but they are over now as quickly as they start. So what! Having panic attacks on odd occasions is part of life for many people. Having an ocasional attack is not diagnosed as panic disorder. It is the fear of them that is the disorder, not the attacks themselves.

No matter how many times I have said this, and I say it constantly, people still set themselves up for another round of panic disorder by saying they are working towards never having another.

Then when they do have one, they think they have failed. Trying to work towards never having another attack is simply not realistic.

I am not being negative. Nor am I saying it is some sort of limitation. It isn't. It is simply how it is. What I haven't ever said to the group, although I do say it publicly, is that I see my attacks now as being very, very healthy! And I am not the only one who sees this. Many of us who have recovered can see how they actually help us. When you lose your fear of it, it still feels violent, but the one big blast it gives us appears to dissolve all the stress and strain we are feeling and leaves us feeling fantastic. As if you have been scrubbed clean inside. We have people who had panic disorder ringing us up and saying, 'I know this sounds stupid, but can you tell me how to have an attack? I know I will feel better if I can have one!' Now that's recovery!!!

When you lose your fear of the attacks, you can really begin to see it as being a gigantic stress release. Some people — even those who still have panic disorder — can feel fantastic after an attack but, because it feels so violent, they are scared of them. I saw a research paper in the early 1980s which discussed this, but at that stage I was still working through my fear and I thought the researchers had no idea what they were talking about. Now I know exactly what they mean. It took me a few years to see this, though!

From: Vicki and Karen
SUBJECT: RECOVERY — COUNTING THE DAYS
Vicki Counting the days is nice but it may not help. How many days are you going to consider is enough to say you have recovered? At the moment you seem to be saying 'I've gone at least twenty days without a panic attack.' A little mind shift needed here?

Karen Wow! Did you just open my eyes! I had actually been keeping a calendar and writing in each day how the day was in terms of panic attacks. I guess I was trying to track my progress, and instead just got caught up in it. It's not living in the present moment at all. It's living in the past and worrying/wondering about the future. 'I did well for twenty days, I wonder how much longer I'll go feeling so good.' I'll try to work on staying in the present moment, and deal with any attack as it comes up.

Vicki I'm trying to remember the last time I felt anxious and panicky, and I can't remember! I have had realistic anxious moments like everyone does but nothing of panic or anxiety (as in disorder) for, well I truly can't remember my last panic attack, it was that long ago.

From: Bronwyn
SUBJECT: RELEARNING
Part of recovery is learning all over again what it feels like to feel 'normal'. It means learning that having a bad day does not mean our anxiety disorder is returning. It means we simply have a bad day, like everyone else in the world!

It also means that if we don't get enough sleep, then we will feel tired and heavy-headed. This doesn't mean that our disorder is returning. It means we didn't get enough sleep.

If we skip meals because we are so busy reclaiming our life, then we may feel dizzy and shaky as a result of skipping meals. It doesn't mean our disorder is returning. It means we are skipping meals and not taking care of ourselves.

Having the flu or another virus can be frightening because so many of the symptoms can mimic our anxiety symptoms. We need to recognise this and not become anxious and fearful that our disorder is returning.

From: Karen
SUBJECT: RELIEF

I think I actually *feel* different. There is a sense of relief lately. Sort of like when you have been holding your breath a long time and you finally exhale. It's not that I don't feel any anxiety or even some near panic, but there is a sense of relaxation about the whole situation. So what if I feel anxious? So what if I panic? I hope I *do* so I can practise and recover some more!

The fear is almost gone, and with that comes a wonderful letting go sensation. My guard is coming down. So what if I shake? So what if I have morning anxiety? It's harmless, it's not a sign of anything worse to come, it will not be around forever, so what?

Bronwyn is right about the mopping-up time. After you 'get it', and it all falls into place, you still find yourself getting anxious, or feeling panicky, or thinking negatively. You even add to it a little sometimes, but now the main difference is you are completely 100% aware of how it is being caused.

Today I woke up and felt slightly anxious, and thought, 'Oh no! I was feeling so great this weekend. What if I feel down again today? What does that mean?' Whoops. Caught myself!

But that real vigilance has lifted. Even after yesterday's minor fender bender, I calmed down, and it didn't put me in a setback. I'm learning that everybody feels anxious and panicky over certain things, but that's not the same as an anxiety disorder. I'm learning to be normal again.

I used to think anxious feelings were 'wrong' even as a child, and that's when I started to fear and avoid those feelings. Now I'm 'changing my perception' about them, and loosening the grip I've had on myself all my life.

From: Angie

SUBJECT: SITTING WITH IT

I have been having some anxiety the last two days too. I know what you mean about the fainting thing, it kind of got to me too. I just decided that it has never happened to me before, and more than likely it is not going to happen now. I remember Bronwyn saying that, if it has never happened before, it won't happen now. In other words, don't buy into it.

For me right now it is just a matter of sitting with whatever is going on or coming up, looking at it and not adding resistance to it. Sometimes I will get that quick surge of panic and start to add fear, and then I just say, no, I am not going to buy into this. Look at it and see where it is coming from and deal with it. Sometimes that is hard but I am working on it. Hang in there, it will get better.

From: Bronwyn

SUBJECT: SYMPTOM SWAPPING

As we move through the recovery process our symptoms will swap and change. This can be frustrating as well as frightening. It is important that we speak to our doctor about any new symptoms. I know that people hesitate, because they do feel like a hypochondriac, but we do need to speak to our doctor about this. If not, we can spend weeks worrying about the new symptom, instead of working through it. And obviously, we do need to know that any new symptom is part of our anxiety disorder!

To help ease our feelings of embarrassment and feelings that we are a hypochondriac, we can ask our doctor to work in partnership with us. We can tell our doctor that we are working through to recovery, and that we need their assistance to enable us to work with any new symptom rather than becoming caught up in further anxiety and panic about it.

From: Karen

SUBJECT: THE ONION

I think my recovery is turning into an issue of trust. Trusting that I can and will recover, I am recovering, trusting that it's only panic disorder and nothing more. Trusting that I will be able to handle whatever comes my way. Trusting that my emotions are safe to feel and not a sign of impending insanity. It's funny how one issue leads to another, and to another and to another. It's the onion! I think I finally get it!

From: Margaret

SUBJECT: THOUGHTS

I am absolutely no expert on separating myself from my thoughts, but I have had a glimpse of what this means while I am meditating. I stress that I still have a long way to go in putting this into practice in the rest of my life when I am really anxious or having a panic attack.

The main thing is that, in meditation, I start to think about something and as soon as I am aware that I'm thinking about something I, gently, without judgment or connecting with the thought, bring myself back to my word. By doing this I can see that it's possible to have thoughts pass through my brain without connecting to them. Sometimes I do drift along with the thoughts for a while before I realise what's happening but the main thing is not to worry just gently bring yourself back to your word or whatever.

I can really sympathise with the disappointment of a setback though, I agree it's very distressing. However, I have found that because I am learning new skills, when I do have a setback I don't sink right back down for long and I seem to get back on track quicker too.

It's funny how this thing takes us up then down then up again. I guess that's recovery. I sort of feel like having anxiety isn't a total 'waste' because I would never have spent the time to get to know myself better had it not been for my anxiety. I agree with Bronwyn that what it takes away you get back ten-fold. Well, I haven't got there yet but I've had a little taste and I like the look of it!!

From: Karen

SUBJECT: WHAT WILL PEOPLE THINK?

I think part of what drives this disorder is the concern over what others think of us, how we appear and what kind of impression we are making. I think the best remedy here is a change in attitude from 'what if?' to *so what!*.

We need to learn how to stop worrying about what others think. Try to remind yourself when you are out, or in any other social situation, that you are there for *yourself*, to buy what you need, to visit a friend, or just to practise, whatever the reason may be.

Tell those worry thoughts you don't *care* what other people think, because you are going to recover and that's what is most important to you. Why worry about what a bunch of complete strangers think of you? They probably aren't even noticing you at all.

Here's a good question: The last time you were at the supermarket, what did the person ahead of you on line look like?? What about the person behind you?? I'm sure you only have a vague recollection, if you remember at all. Why?? Because you were too concerned with yourself, your items, the other things you needed to do that day, how long the line was taking. Guess what?? Everybody else was wrapped up in themselves, too!!

From: Bronwyn
SUBJECT: WHAT WILL PEOPLE THINK?

We all wear quite a number of 'masks' during the day and while we are very adept at changing our 'masks' in any situation it can become very confusing. We may be with someone we consider a good friend and we can be wearing this particular 'good friend' mask, and while we are together we meet an acquaintance. We can then feel anxious. We need to be ' all we can be to our friend', but we also 'need to be all we can be' to fit in with how we think our acquaintance 'needs us to be' and that may be completely different from who we need to be to our friend. It is far simpler and less anxiety-provoking just to be our self!

From: Lorrie
SUBJECT: WHO TO TELL?

I know it seems like the hardest thing to do sometimes, but why not be honest and explain that you have anxiety attacks? I may be stepping out of line here but I truly believe, through lots of experience in being more up front about my disorder in the last two years, that people understand so much more than we give them credit for.

I know I've mentioned this before, but I can't tell you how many people, once I explained I have panic attacks, went on to tell me how they know so and so who also does or, more often than I could have ever expected, that they themselves do in certain situations, and so on. And, those who don't often said to me that it was so nice to know now why I didn't always do things, and that it wasn't just because I didn't want to be with them or their group. I found them very willing to cooperate with what I needed for my recovery process. Just a thought!

UPON REFLECTION

When the wind blows
the fields of golden velvet bow in reverence

When the sun shines
the fields of golden velvet parade shamelessly

When the rain falls
the fields of golden velvet drink until their
thirst is quenched

When dusk descends
the fields of golden velvet surrender

The fields of golden velvet
are wiser than I.

Carolyn Barker

CHAPTER 11

THE THIRD LAYER

From: Karen

SUBJECT: SNEAKY THOUGHTS

This thought alone, 'Will I be able to cope?, Will I get sick?', could be causing and keeping your anxiety hanging around. Cognitive behavioural therapy is great for working with the obvious thoughts, especially during panic, such as 'I'm going crazy' or 'I'm having a heart attack!' These thoughts are easy to catch because they are 'loud', so to speak.

But it's the very 'quiet', vague, and more sneaky thoughts, like 'Will I be able to cope?' or 'Will I ever recover?' or 'What do my family and friends think of me?' that are big anxiety producers.

You can know a lot intellectually from CBT. For instance, you say you know you have coped in the past. But it takes time and experience to know it emotionally, on a gut level, to finally believe it down in your bones. Until you believe it in your bones, you will experience anxiety and panic.

It's like the old saying, 'no pain, no gain'. In order to recover from panic and anxiety, you must feel them without adding fear, until you know in your bones that there is no 'ultimate' attack waiting to get you. There is nothing horrible about to happen, hence nothing to fear.

It sounds to me, that you have hit a wall in recovery. That wall is the fear, apprehension and hesitation to take risks. You know in your head, panic can't hurt you, but yet you still avoid situations that may cause you to panic. Why? Because you don't feel safe. Some part of you is still afraid.

Medication works for some people, but you can't medicate your habitual thought patterns of fear, avoidance and worry. If a drug could do that, the entire world would be taking it! You have tried so many different drugs. I think the reason why you have hit a plateau in recovery has to do with something you are thinking, something you are still fearing.

The first stage of recovery is developing our mindfulness skills. We become aware of our panic and anxiety-producing thoughts, and we see how they create our symptoms. We learn to see we have a choice in either becoming involved with them or letting them go.

As our mindfulness skills increase, we see not only the 'loud' panic anxiety-producing thoughts, but we become aware of the second layer of them. This second layer shows us how our thoughts can activate our anxiety in ordinary everyday situations.

As our mindfulness skills develop further, we see yet another layer of thoughts. These thoughts show us how our need for approval permeates our life. We see how we are invalidating ourselves by not caring or being responsible for ourselves, and we see how this creates much of our underlying anxiety and depression.

From: Group member

SUBJECT: BIG SETBACK

I'm having a setback. I've had the flu for three days and I feel terrible. I was in bed for the first two days because I had a high temperature and felt generally lousy. I was supposed to have a session with my anxiety coach yesterday. I called her and told her not to come, because I still wasn't feeling fit enough to work on my avoidance behaviour.

She insisted that I have my session and so she came over. I spoke to her and told her I just wasn't well enough. But she insisted again so we went out. We walked a couple of blocks and I told her I was feeling awful. Not panic anxiety awful, but flu awful. I told her, but all she did was to tell me to walk across the road and walk down the street by myself and she would meet me at the next set of traffic lights. So I walked across the road and then I had a massive panic attack. I met her at the traffic lights and she walked me back to my place, but now I feel as if I am back to square one. I have been anxious since then and I can't get control of it.

She rang me today to remind me that I had to go out and practise my avoidance behaviour. I had already planned to do that, and I was going to have lunch with my friend at a cafe nearby. But all morning I was so anxious and when I got to the cafe I couldn't eat. That panic attack yesterday has taken away all my confidence. I am back to where I started. Now I have to start all over again. This seems all too hopeless.

From: Bronwyn

SUBJECT: BIG SETBACK

No, it isn't. Let's break this down. Having the flu at anytime is awful, but when we have an anxiety disorder it seems so much worse. Many of the symptoms of flu are similar to our anxiety symptoms and sometimes we can't tell the difference between them. Many people think they are having a setback when they have the flu, whereas if they really looked at it they would accept that they have the flu and wouldn't fight against it. They would simply let themselves be sick.

This panic attack is not your everyday 'loud thought' panic attack. While your thoughts have triggered it, this panic attack is a result of you invalidating and not respecting yourself.

You were not feeling well. You felt pressured to do your exposure work, although you had told your coach that you did not feel well enough to go out. She didn't respect the fact that you were not feeling well. So you went out with her, knowing that this was not a good time for you to be doing this. You were trying to be the 'perfect' client. When you told her again how terrible you felt, she didn't acknowledge it, but probably thought you were getting caught up in your panic and anxiety.

You crossed the street at her behest and you had the panic attack. But if you check your thoughts, I think they would be saying to you something along the lines of, 'I don't want to do this. I just feel too sick. I want to go home and go to bed. Why is she making me do this? She knows I am not well.'

When we invalidate ourselves like this, we are going to be anxious and we can have a panic attack. Not only were you invalidating yourself, you were allowing her to invalidate you by not insisting that you cancel the session.

Because you can't see the reason for this panic attack, you have become caught up in the normal panic anxiety thinking. 'What if I have another attack like that? Why can't I recover? Why can't I get it right?' And this thinking is now contaminating everything else you want to do, including lunch with your friend.

If you had realised yesterday the reason you had the panic attack, today could have been a completely different experience. You would have seen that it was a reaction to you invalidating yourself, and your thinking would not have rolled over into the normal panic anxiety thinking. When we are working through to recovery, we need to become mindful of when we are invalidating ourselves, and where we need to put a boundary.

In this instance, you needed to set a boundary to protect yourself. You had flu, and you knew that going out with your anxiety coach was going to be more difficult because you were not feeling well. Being able to say 'no' to your coach is skilful compassionate action.

If people have a problem with that, well, it is their problem, not yours! They will 'need to get over it'. You don't need to get over it to please them, or to be the perfect client or perfect person. Their thoughts are their responsibility, not yours. If they don't approve, that is their responsibility, not yours. Your responsibility is to you and your recovery.

The need to belong

We need to become aware of our subtle thoughts and behaviours. We will see how our anxiety and panic can increase when we are not respecting ourselves, or being responsible for our own needs.

When we say 'yes' and mean 'no', our anxiety and feelings of panic can increase. They can increase when we take responsibility for everyone's feelings, and when we go out of our way to make everyone feel happy. We will see how our fear of hurting or upsetting people in the slightest way increases our anxiety.

We will see how we are constantly feeling guilty. We will also see our perfectionist behaviour and how this impacts on everything we do, including being the perfect patient, and we will see how this generates anxiety and panic.

When we can see this, it creates confusion, because what can we do? We can let these subtle thoughts go, but we feel as if we are in a no-win situation, because we feel as if there is nothing we can do about our overall circumstances. We feel trapped.

When we are aware of this, we can choose to continue as we have been doing, or we can become fully responsible for ourselves by taking our foot off the brakes completely! In doing so we allow our emotional development to unfold and we develop a more authentic, real sense of self and identity. We belong to ourselves rather than 'needing to belong'. Taking this step can generate further fears:

- This is selfish.
- This is not caring for others.
- This is egotistical.
- I can't do this.
- I won't be able to do this.
- This it is too hard.
- I'm scared I'll fail.
- What if I do fail?
- I'd rather not try in the first place because I couldn't bear it if I did fail.
- People will think I am stupid.
- What if I do succeed, what will happen to me? I'll be different from everyone else.

Can you see the central theme in these fears? They come back to a core fear: 'What will people think of me?'

I've found in the workshops I run that it is helpful to put this stage of recovery into a specific framework. This way we can see and understand where we are, and where skilful action can take us. As a starting point, I draw upon the work of Abraham Maslow and Ken Wilber.

Abraham Maslow is credited as being the pioneer in humanist and existential psychology. And Ken Wilber is a leading theorist in the study of human consciousness. Maslow developed a hierarchy of 'self needs' which demonstrates our potential development throughout life (Maslow 1954). This hierarchy can be our guide to understanding where we are and how we can develop further emotionally.

Maslow's hierarchy of needs is:

6. Self-transcendence
5. Self-actualisation
4. Self-esteem needs
3. The need to belong
2. Safety needs
1. Survival needs

Development in these terms means we need to be able to satisfy the set of needs at each level of the hierarchy or 'ladder' before we can develop further. Ken Wilber, who writes extensively on this subject, proposes an overall model of development based on a spectrum of consciousness — in other words, based on a greater expansion of personal awareness.

That is, as we move through each level of development 'each set of needs . . . the self will eventually grow beyond these views and expand its awareness' (Wilber 1996). The operative word is 'expand'. The more aware we become, the more our perception of our self unfolds. In doing so, as Wilber states, we 'step off the present rung, disidentify with it, and then identify with the next higher rung'.

The first set of needs in Maslow's hierarchy are our physiological (survival) needs. We need air to breathe, we need nourishment and obviously these needs have been met!

As they have been met, the next set of needs comes into play and these are our safety needs, both personal and environmental. For most of us these basic needs have been met, athough people who were abused as children may still have personal safety issues that need to be resolved. At this level we may be at an impasse as adults, and find ourselves in relationships where the abuse from childhood is carried over into adult relationships. If this is the case, being able to meet our personal safety needs becomes part of the work we need to do.

The next set of needs is the 'need to belong'. We need to belong to our families, our peer group and society as a whole. We need to be liked and loved. And this is where we all 'live'. We are still trying to find a sense of belonging. Our way of trying to meet this set of needs means we have given away any sense of personal self, any sense of personal power, as we try to meet the expectations of who we think we should be. If we can become who we think we should be, people will think well of us, and if they do think well of us then we can belong.

At this level in the hierarchy, we feel there is no room for us to move in order to address the self-esteem needs. Self-esteem needs demand much from us, and they are in direct opposition to the need to belong. Figure 1 outlines the differences between these two ways of being. From our vantage point within the hierarchy, the demands of self-esteem are frightening to contemplate. It brings in all our fears of not being likeable, of not being lovable, of not belonging. It also calls into question our 'rules' about who we should be, about compassion and what selfishness really means. From this level on the 'ladder' our awareness does not enable us to see the 'bigger picture'.

Figure 1 NEED TO BELONG VERSUS SELF-ESTEEM

Need to belong	Assumption/outcome	Self-esteem — skilful action
Saying yes when I mean no	I have no choice	Saying no when we mean no
If I say no to people I am being selfish	I have no right to put my needs first	Being honest with self and others
If I say no to people they will be hurt	I hurt my self instead by saying yes	Saying no is being responsible for myself
If I say no to people I feel guilty	Which confirms my worst fears about myself	Treating our self with respect
If I say no to people they may not like me	I am rejecting myself	Honouring ourselves
When I say yes to peole I feel resentful	Why does it always have to be me?	Seeing we have a choice in what we do and say
When I say yes to people I feel used	I will feel angry at myself and them	It is our responsibility to make a choice
When I say yes to people I smile	I don't want people to feel it is an imposition	We are not responsible for other people's feelings
When I say yes to people I feel stressed	I should be able to handle it	Not creating unnecessary stress for ourselves
I can always see different points of view	But I am unsure which view to take	Respecting our own opinions
I can't make a decision	I know what I want, but is it the same as what others want?	Trusting our opinions
I go out of my way to make sure everyone is happy	Isn't this what I am supposed to do?	Being responsible for our feelings
I always try to be perfect in everything I do	Is there any other way?	Honouring ourselves and our abilities
I help people all the time, but when I need it they don't have time to help me	I feel confused and rejected	Having realistic expectations of self and others
I never get angry at other people	Only at myself	Learning anger's hidden message about our perceptions and expectations of ourselves and other people
I don't cry	I should be able to handle anything	Feeling and expressing our emotions

Need to belong	Assumption/outcome	Self-esteem — skilful action
If I do cry I feel stupid	Because it shows that I am weak	Expressing our emotions is healthy
I always help others at work even though it puts me way behind	People expect this from me	Being responsible for our time management
I feel so ashamed when people criticise me	I try to be as perfect as I can	Being able to look at the validity of the criticism; taking it on board if applicable, or setting a boundary
People ring me all hours of the day wanting my help	I am never sure why they ask me	Respecting our needs, time and abilities
My partner gets upset with me when other people want my help; I should give more time to my family	It makes me anxious trying to choose who I give time to	Finding a healthy balance
I cannot spend time just sitting, reading or relaxing	There is always too much to do	Taking time to relax and enjoy quiet time with our self
I can't spend time alone	It makes me feel nervous for some reason	Feeling comfortable with self
My needs and wants don't count	Do I have any?	Aware of our needs and wants and meeting them
I always do what everyone wants	Isn't this what I am supposed to do?	Knowing and saying no when we want to
I can't say what I want to do	Everyone will think it is stupid	Being assertive
I can't speak up at meetings	I do not want to look like an idiot	Treating self with dignity
I have ideas but don't say anything; then someone else has the same idea and puts it forward; it is always accepted without question	This always amazes me. They aren't treated like idiots	Respecting my ideas and opinions
I can't ask questions	People will think I am stupid	Asking questions is how we learn
I can't speak in public	I will make a fool of myself	Why will I?
I feel so different from everyone else	I try so hard to be like everyone else	Being ourselves and honouring the differences

Need to belong	Assumption/outcome	Self-esteem — skilful action
I do not have a choice in anything I do	There is a choice?	Seeing there is always a choice
I can't identify my feelings	I shouldn't have feelings	Identifying and feeling our feelings
I can't bear people around me being angry or annoyed	I feel as if it is my fault	Separating ourselves psychologically from other people
I feel smothered by other people	I shouldn't feel like this	Setting a boundary
I am the peacekeeper in the family	It is my responsibility	Not taking care of other people's problems
When my partner says he/she loves me, I don't believe him/her	I don't like me, I loathe myself, I hate myself	Treating ourselves with care and respect
I do not believe people if they say they like me	How can they?	Accepting ourselves
If I'm told I am doing a good job at work, I don't believe it	I worry that people will find out that I'm a fraud	Acknowledging our intelligence and skills
I have never thought of myself as intelligent	I am stupid, dumb, hopeless	This isn't intelligent thinking
I try never to make a mistake	So people won't know I am hopeless	Learning from my mistakes
I can't understand why I have an anxiety disorder	I try so hard to be perfect	I can!

Self-esteem needs demand a different way of looking at ourselves and the world around us. At this level, it is not so much the need to belong, the need to be liked or loved by everyone, it is the need to belong to ourselves.

If we are unable to meet our self-esteem needs, it is going to be difficult for us to reach our full potential at the self-actualisation level. At the moment, all our energy is being used to keep us where we think we should be, not where we could be. We have so little to give to meet our potential because our need to belong sabotages any attempts we make to realise this level. After all, what will people think?

The last set of needs on Maslow's hierarchy is the need for self transcendence. This means going beyond the personal sense of self and beginning to identity with the spiritual self. But that is another book entirely!

As I discussed in the beginning, the more aware we become, the more we will see how our daily interactions with other people create so much of our anxiety. This is when our anxiety can become our teacher if we allow it to. We will see how we do not accept ourselves, our needs and wants and how we are violating our responsibility to ourselves. This in turn generates our feelings of worthlessness and helplessness.

Anxiety as our teacher

From: Group member

SUBJECT: GOOD NICE PERSON

I really need help in trying to work out how to work through the whole situation with my mother. It feels as if I am damned if I do, and damned if I don't.

There are three people involved in this. My sister, my mother and me. My sister has the same difficulties as I do with our mother. We both try to keep our distance from her as much as possible as she has always been very manipulative. But between us we try to make sure everything is all right for her. The rest of the family have moved interstate and overseas so there isn't anyone else to do this.

This is the situation that happened the other day. My sister and her children went to visit Mum. Her video recorder had broken down so my sister offered to take it and have it repaired. I saw my sister a few days later, and she asked if I would mind taking it back to Mum. I live about a mile away from Mum, and my sister lives on the other side of town. She didn't put any pressure on me to do this, because we both understand how it can be with Mum, but I didn't have a problem in taking it back to her. I took the recorder to Mum's on the way to the hairdressers. And it was a disaster as usual. The conversation went something like this

'Isn't she coming to see me? How can I give her the money for getting it fixed?' I said, 'She told you not to worry about that. She said she would pay for it.'

Mum said, 'I've got the cash out of the bank today. I want to pay her now.' And I replied, 'She said she would pay for it. You can deposit the money back in your account next time you go to the bank.'

Then Mum said: 'I don't want to go back to the bank. You can take her the money. I want you to take the money to her now.' She gave me this disgusted look.

She's been giving me this look ever since I was a kid. It is meant to make me do what she wants me to do.

I said to her, 'I've got an appointment and I don't have time to drive over there today.' And Mum said, 'I don't want to keep the money in the house. I'll be very nervous. I won't be able to sleep.' I try and trade off with her. 'I will take the money and give it to her when I see her later next week.'

Then Mum told me, 'I want to pay her now, not next week. Maybe Joe (my mother's friend) will drive me over so I can pay her now. I'll phone Joe to see if he can help me with this.'

I am beginning to feel guilty, because I don't want to involve my mother's friend in this. What is he going to think of me not doing this for Mum? Now he has to do it and it is my fault. All I was doing was a favour to my sister. Now I get demands of 'do this' and 'do it right now' put on me. My guilt is getting stronger and I am feeling really anxious. And then I think, well, it is only twenty-five minutes drive in the car. It isn't such a big deal.

Anyone would think I am horrible for not doing it. It will save everyone else the trouble and Mum won't lie awake worrying about it if I do this. I can cancel my hair appointment. But I don't want to cancel it, because I really need a haircut.

So I told her to give me the money and I would take it to my sister later on. But she wouldn't give it to me. She wanted it done now. I know it was wrong, but we were getting nowhere, so I left and went to the hairdresser. I felt so selfish. I could always get my hair done later.

This is another incident: Mum rang me and told me she was lonely and bored. We were in the middle of painting the house so there wasn't anything I could do to help her. So, I asked her if she wanted to go to the kids' school fundraising day the following weekend. I said I was going through the cupboards to see what I could give the school to sell at the fundraiser. I asked her if she had anything she could donate and we could take it when we went.

Mum rang me an hour later to say she had been through all her cupboards and she had quite a few things she could donate. I thanked her, then she told me to come and get it straight away. She had taken it all out and now it was cluttering up her house. Even though I had an excuse not to go over there straightaway, because we were painting, she was furious and so was I.

It is her lack of respect for me that makes me so angry! I know I shouldn't be but

I can't help it. She doesn't give me a choice and I feel so guilty. She makes me feel so guilty about so many things.

When she gets angry at me, she rings everyone up and I mean everyone. Everyone here, everyone who lives interstate and everyone who lives overseas. Then everyone rings me, to remind me I need to take care of her, or to let me know she is ringing everyone and telling them. I just feel so bad.

What is the guilt about specifically? Can you see where I am getting caught and what I need to look at here? Is it that I am wanting to save other people from what my mother does to me? Or is it because everyone will be thinking I am selfish and horrible? Am I trying to avoid their and the world's disapproval?

This sort of thing happens all the time. I am tired of feeling guilty and anxious all the time. I am even thinking about moving interstate just to get away from it all. What can I do about this?

'This sort of thing happens all the time.' It does, doesn't it? But we don't need to leave town to get away from it all. We 'get away from it all' by skilful compassionate action.

As I have said before, compassion is non-violation to self and to others. What we don't realise is that our need to be all things to all people is not compassionate or skilful, either for ourselves or for others.

Let's look at this email and see how the practice of skilful action can be used effectively to break through our anxiety and guilt and can assist us in meeting our own self esteem needs, while leaving people the opportunity to meet theirs.

Member I really need help in trying to work out how to work through the whole situation with my mother. It feels as if I am damned if I do, and damned if I don't. There are three people involved in this. My sister, my mother and me. My sister has the same difficulties as I do with our mother. We both try to keep our distance from her as much as possible as she has always been very manipulative. But between us we try to make sure everything is all right for her. The rest of the family have moved interstate and overseas so there isn't anyone else to do this.

Bronwyn *You are aware your mother can be very manipulative but how are you dealing with this? People can be manipulative, but it depends on your attitude to her manipulation. You have a choice in this. You can take it on board, by taking responsibility for her manipulation by feeling guilty, resentful and bitter, which in turn will bring on the anxiety. Or if you recognise and accept the manipulation as simply your mother being your mother then it will not be a problem. You simply accept this as being part of who she is.*

Member But between us we try to make sure everything is all right for her.

Bronwyn *If you are doing this because you want to, there is no problem with this. You won't be thinking about it in a way that generates anxiety and guilt. If you are doing this because you think you 'should', then you will not only be feeling anxious, you may also be feeling resentful and perhaps bitter towards her. Then you will in all probability feel guilty because you feel this way, and round and round you go.*

Making sure everything is all right for her means ensuring she is okay, physically and mentally. If she is sick, this means making sure she has medical attention. Or if she needs housework, shopping, gardening or house repairs done, it means arranging for someone to come and do it. It doesn't mean it is your responsibility to do it all.

If you want to help, then it isn't an issue, but if you feel as if you have to you will feel angry, resentful and guilty for feeling this way and you will feel anxious. If this is so, then you need to be able to reframe this, otherwise it will continue to impact on your relationship with your mother. Although part of you may feel you don't want to do any of this, on the other hand not doing it can also be a violation of your own integrity, a violation of your own morality and ethics. If so, you can change your perception, knowing that you want to do this because you are honouring your own principles.

Member This is the situation that happened the other day. My sister and her children went to visit Mum. Her video recorder had broken down so my sister offered to take it and have it repaired. I saw my sister a few days later, and she asked if I would mind taking it back to Mum. I live about a mile away from Mum, and my sister lives on the other side of town. She didn't put any pressure on me to do this, because we both understand how it can be with Mum, but I didn't have a problem in taking it back to her. I took the recorder to Mum's on the way to the hairdressers. And it was a disaster as usual.

Bronwyn *Your sister gave you a choice and because you didn't mind, it wasn't a problem. If you felt you didn't have a choice, and you thought to yourself, 'I have to do this. Why is it always me? My sister offered to get it fixed, she should take it back', you could become anxious. Again, it is your attitude and the way you are thinking about the particular situation which may or may not generate anxiety.*

Member The conversation went something like this.

Mum *Isn't she coming to see me? How can I give her the money for getting it fixed?*

Member She told you not to worry about that. She said she would pay for it.

Bronwyn *This is between your mum and your sister and in this exchange you are not taking responsibility for either of them. You are simply stating it how it is. And this is how it needs to be.*

Mum I've got the cash out of the bank today. I want to pay her now.

Member *She said she would pay for it. You can deposit the money back in your account next time you go to the bank.*

Bronwyn *Again, in this you are not taking responsibility. Nor do you need to. What you are doing, and rightly so, is giving the responsibility back to your mother by suggesting she re-bank the monies next time she is at the bank.*

Mum I don't want to go back to the bank. You can take her the money. I want you to take the money to her now.

Member *She gave me this disgusted look. She's been giving me this look ever since I was a kid. It is meant to make me do what she wants me to do.*

Bronwyn Your mother doesn't want to go back to the bank. This is what she wants. It has nothing to do with you, if you don't want it to be. It is her responsibility in what she wants and doesn't want, and it is her responsibility as to what she does with the money.

In regards to the 'disgusting' look she gave you. You know why she is doing it, and you also know that she knows how it is going to effect you. And it does. The look she gives you takes you straight back to childhood thoughts and feelings: 'I am disgusting.' Do you feel shame? Do you feel guilty? Did you begin to feel anxious? As a child you didn't know you were not disgusting. You didn't know you had nothing to be ashamed about. You didn't know you had nothing to feel guilty about.

Now you are an adult and you need to look at this as an adult. When you go back into the thinking and feeling state of childhood, you are not being responsible for you. When you are being responsible for you, you recognise that you are not disgusting, you know that you have nothing to be ashamed about, nothing to be guilty about. You recognise and accept that this is how your mother gets her wants and needs met.

It doesn't mean you are a terrible person or she is a terrible person. It is simply her way of trying to get her way. When you are being responsible for yourself, you see the reality and simply accept this is how your mother is.

Member *I've got an appointment and I don't have time to drive over there today.*

Bronwyn You are accepting responsibility for what you want to do, and you are accepting responsibility for how you manage your time.

Mum *I don't want to keep the money in the house. I'll be very nervous. I won't be able to sleep.*

Bronwyn This is your mother's responsibility and is part of her manipulation. It is her nervousness and she is aware she will not sleep if she worries. What can she do about this to ensure she does sleep? This is her responsibility, not yours.

Member *I try and trade off with her. 'I will take the money and give it to her when I see her later next week.'*

Bronwyn This is actually not a 'trade off' unless you feel resentful about it. You are giving your mother an option. It is a compromise which doesn't compromise your self. If you feel resentful, then you are compromising yourself, because you are taking responsibility for your mother and letting go of the responsibility for yourself. When we compromise ourselves we become anxious. 'I don't want to do this. Why is it always me?' These thoughts generate anxiety. If you are compromising yourself, it would be better for both you and your mother not to take the money. This way you let both yourself and your mother 'off the hook'. You won't feel resentful and this will not 'contaminate' your relationship with your mother.

Mum *I want to pay her now, not next week. Maybe Joe (my mother's friend) will drive me over so I can pay her now. I'll phone Joe to see if he can help me with this.*

Member I am beginning to feel guilty, because I don't want to involve my mother's friend in this. What is he going to think of me not doing this for Mum? Now he has to do it and it is my fault.

Bronwyn *Why is it your fault? Why are you feeling guilty? You have nothing to feel guilty about. Whose moral code are you breaking? Your mother's? Your mother's friend's? This is your mother's problem. It is her responsibility not yours. If she rings her friend, then it is up to her friend to say either yes or no.*

You can't take responsibility for your mother's friend and how he feels about this. What he thinks about you is up to him. Look at what you are already feeling in trying to have him think well of you. Feeling guilty is always a sign you are not being responsible for yourself.

Member All I was doing was a favour to my sister. Now I get demands of 'do this' and 'do it right now' put on me. My guilt is getting stronger and I am feeling really anxious. And then I think, well, it is only twenty-five minutes drive in the car. It isn't such a big deal.

Anyone would think I am horrible for not doing it. It will save everyone else the trouble and Mum won't lie awake worrying about it if I do this. I can cancel my hair appointment. But I don't want to cancel it, because I really need a haircut.

So I told her to give me the money and I would take it to my sister later on. But she wouldn't give it to me. She wanted it done now. I know it was wrong, but we were getting nowhere, so I left and went to the hairdresser. I felt so selfish. I could always get my hair done later.

Bronwyn *Why was it wrong? Why are you feeling selfish? Why are you horrible? Look at how you are feeling about yourself. Is it any wonder you are feeling anxious?*

All you were doing was a favour to your sister. But look at how it has escalated because you are taking responsibility for how other people think, feel and act.

This isn't a small thing because it is part of the 'bigger' picture. As you say this sort of thing happens all the time. Saving other people trouble, your mother and her friend, is being responsible for them, it is not being responsible for yourself. You are not responsible for what people think about, and how they react.

If other people think you are horrible, well, this is what they think. There is nothing you can do about it. But how do you know your mother's friend will think you are horrible? Is it really because you think you are horrible for not doing this? You also need to be aware that the 'trade-off' in needing people to think well of you versus your own wants and needs is anxiety and sometimes panic and depression.

Member This is another incident: Mum rang me and told me she was lonely and bored. We were in the middle of painting the house so there wasn't anything I could do to help her. So, I asked her if she wanted to go to the kids' school fundraising day the following weekend. I said I was going through the cupboards to see what I could give the school to sell at the fundraiser. I asked her if she had anything she could donate and we could take it when we went.

Bronwyn *This is for your mum to work out what she can do to ease her loneliness and boredom. You are not responsible for how she feels, nor are you responsible for making her happy. Asking her to go with you to the fundraiser was great, so long as you didn't ask her because you felt guilty about how she was feeling. This is only going to create resentment and, as I said before, it can 'contaminate' your overall relationship with her.*

Member Mum rang me an hour later to say she had been through all her cupboards and she had quite a few things she could donate. I thanked her, then she told me to come and get it straight away. She had taken it all out, and now it was cluttering up her house. Even though I had an excuse not to go over there straight-away, because we were painting, she was furious and so was I.

Bronwyn *You didn't need an excuse. You were painting. It is that simple. Your mother knew you were painting the house. She chose to go through her cupboards that day, although she knew the fundraiser was a week away. Your mother could have delayed doing this, or she could have put them all together and put them in a spare room or in the garage.*

Your mother was furious. This is her reaction and her responsibility, not yours. Why were you furious? This is your reaction and it is your responsibility. It comes back to you being able to accept that this is how your mother is. You can't change her. When you can accept this, her fury, along with her looks of disgust, will bounce off you. You can certainly feel for her about being lonely and bored, but it is not your responsibility to fix it.

Member It is her lack of respect for me that drives me so angry! I know I shouldn't be but I can't help it.

Bronwyn *Why 'shouldn't' you be angry? Who says you 'shouldn't'. Your anger is a defence against her lack of respect, but what you are not seeing is that you are not respecting yourself. Because you are buying into her manipulations, you are strug-gling with respecting your self. You are not accepting you, nor are you accepting that you have needs and wants of your own.*

Member She doesn't give me a choice and I feel so guilty.

Bronwyn *She may try not to give you a choice, but you have one all the same.*

Member She makes me feel so guilty about so many things.

Bronwyn: *She doesn't make you feel guilty. Although we don't see it, it is our decision, our choice, to feel guilty. Look at it this way. Whose moral code are you breaking? Where is it written in your 'life description' that you are a 'sacrificial lamb'?*

Member When she gets angry at me, she rings everyone up and I mean everyone. Everyone here, everyone who lives interstate and everyone who lives overseas. Then everyone rings me, to remind me I need to take care of her, or to let me know she is ringing everyone and telling them. I just feel so bad.

Bronwyn *Again it comes back to why are you feeling bad? She is ringing them, probably knowing they will ring you, knowing you will feel bad and guilty, so you will do what she wants. Everyone who rings you may or may not be aware of the dynamics of the situation. Whether they are aware or not, it is still your decision to buy into feeling bad and guilty.*

Member What is the guilt about specifically? Can you see where I am getting caught and what I need to look at here? Is it that I am wanting to save other people from what my mother does to me? Or is it because everyone will be thinking I am selfish and horrible? Am I trying to avoid their and the world's disapproval?

This sort of thing happens all the time. I am tired of feeling guilty and anxious all the time. I am even thinking about moving interstate just to get away from it all. What can I do about this?

Bronwyn *Do you realise how much all of this contributes to your ongoing anxiety? All of the above! But your mother is 'not doing this to you'. You aren't seeing you have a choice. She can try to make you feel 'bad' and guilty' but it is up to you whether you take this on. Bottom line: you are still trying to be the 'good nice dutiful daughter', the way she wants you to be, and the way you think the world wants you to be. 'Good nice dutiful daughters' are not being who they could be, with all the responsibilities to themselves that this entails.*

When you are trying to move towards a more secure sense of self, with its inherent mental health, the ingrained 'good dutiful' daughter is going to feel guilty. This is not how 'she' thinks she should be. One disgusting look can dissolve any intention of moving away psychologically from your mother, because the authentic you is not yet established. So the guilt saves you from 'emotionally' leaving your mother and other people. Feeling guilty means you try to save other people by being responsible for them, and this way it saves you from other people's disapproval. And you are trapped. Game, set and match!

The questions are: What do you need and want for you? What can you do to meet these needs without taking on the responsibility for your mother and other people?

What can you do when your mother manipulates and others disapprove of you? What can you do to create a safe environment for you, without having to leave town? And: How do you do this without feeling guilty? By skilful compassionate action — by being responsible for yourself, accepting and respecting your self and your needs.

Guilt

Does this sound familiar? Don't we get caught in situations like this ? And it can become quite complex because, every time we turn around, there is someone else's feelings to consider — or that we think we have to consider. Where are our own needs in this? They have taken a 'back seat'. Even if we do meet our own needs, any sense of respecting ourselves is gone. We are too busy beating ourselves up, thinking we are selfish, horrible or 'disgusting'. Is it any wonder we feel anxious?

But we can actually use our anxiety in a constructive way. We can learn from it, and we can ultimately defeat our anxiety, by using it to see where we are not accepting and being responsible for ourselves. When we can see this, we are then able to become more skilful in our thoughts and actions towards ourselves and other people.

Part of these skilful actions is learning where to set boundaries. A boundary can be either physical or psychological, or both. These are used to define who we are. Setting and keeping our boundaries protects us from our own and other peoples' expectations and perceptions of who we should be.

As an example: when we are standing in a queue and someone comes and stands right next to us, we feel they are invading our 'space' so we take a step away from them to protect that space. When we do this we are setting a physical boundary. If we are in a physically abusive relationship, we need to set physical boundaries to protect ourselves from being abused. And this may mean that we leave the abusive situation permanently.

Psychologically, we take on board whatever anyone says to us. We don't look at it, examine it and see if what they are saying is true for us. Even if we don't think it is true for us, we take it on board and adjust our perceptions and behaviour to suit.

Setting a psychological boundary means we don't take everything on board. We look at it, examine it and, if it is not valid or true for us, then we don't become involved with it or go along with it to placate others. In this way we define ourselves and our perceptions and opinions by separating ourselves from other people's perceptions and opinions.

It can be difficult and frightening to set boundaries because we have been taught that compassion means taking care of everyone's feelings and meeting their wants and needs. This is what most of us think compassion means. But it doesn't! Compassion is no harm to self or others but, in the above example, the conflicting feelings of our group member were certainly harmful to her. If our group member had had psychological boundaries in place, she would not have become caught up in feeling horrible, selfish, guilty or anxious. She would have been able to see the situation exactly for what is was — her mother's way of trying to have her needs met. With boundaries in place, the group member would have been able to separate herself from the manipulation, instead of becoming caught up in it.

We don't see the harm we do to ourselves and other people from our perspective at the 'need to belong' level of Maslow's hierarchy of needs. We aren't seeing the 'bigger picture'. When we are responsible for other people, we don't give them the opportunity to see and examine the reasons for their own expectations, annoyances, anger, frustration and all their other feelings that can cause them pain and suffering. People may not want to take responsibility for themselves, but this is their choice. It doesn't mean we need to step in and do it for them.

In some instances, skilful compassionate action means standing back. Sometimes, our actions in being responsible for other people; in trying to 'rescue' other people, unknowingly contribute to their situation or circumstances.

From Group member
SUBJECT: NO-WIN SITUATION
I would really like to not only be able to say yes or no, depending on how I really felt; I would really like to be able to know how I really felt about whatever it is I am saying yes or no to. I want to say no, but I can't. If I say no, I am letting people down and I feel really guilty. When I say yes I feel frustrated and angry at myself. It is a no-win situation.

Guilt is a passive emotion and comes with the 'package' of being all things to all people. It is a by-product of our lack of acceptance for ourselves and our own needs. And this is the reason we can have difficulty knowing exactly what our needs are.

We can feel guilty about anything. We may have a conversation with someone, and then review the conversation in our mind. We can worry about the inflection in our voice, in case the person has taken what we said the 'wrong' way. We can worry about our facial expression in case other people 'read' something into it that wasn't there. We worry that we should be doing this, or shouldn't have done that. We feel guilty if we don't meet our expectations of who we think we should be, if we are not meeting other people's expectations of us.

Expectations

From: Eric
SUBJECT: EXPECTATIONS
This evening I had a couple of new realisations, both to do with my low self-esteem. The first is a need to justify myself whenever someone questions something about me — for example, my beliefs or the way I live. I always feel the need to justify myself, to clarify things. Underlying this are thoughts and feelings that, 'I have to prevent them from thinking I'm nuts' or 'what if they got a wrong impression of me'. This way, I am always putting myself on the defensive, instead of not being bothered with someone else's views or perception of things! I do not need other people's approval!!

The second realisation is that I am projecting expectations onto other people, and then I am disappointed, annoyed, irritated or angry when those expectations are not fulfilled. I'm really realising now, more and more, that I can't expect other people to provide happiness for me.

From: Jill
SUBJECT: EXPECTATIONS
These are the same expectations I had of others. They needed to be just like me, same ideas, morals, and on, and on I went. How exhausting! Now I can accept that not everyone will like me. I don't like everyone, but I do respect them. It's such a powerful feeling, Eric, when you accept this.

You can just move through situations that used to be tiring and traumatic mentally. You are so right when you say we need to create our own happiness, no one else can do that for us. I have personally found this part of recovery the most powerful aspect yet.

From: Bronwyn
SUBJECT: EXPECTATIONS

I was thinking about this, in so far as what we consider to be our expectations of our self, and how we try to live up to them. And what I realised was that we all have a sense of 'pride' in our expectations, however unrealistic they may be. At least we have them! We can continue to beat ourselves up when we can't meet them, then we can continue to be anxious, and round and round we go!

And while we are doing this, we are discounting the reality of our own experience by discounting our intelligence, our skills, our talents and our individual qualities and our interactions with others.

We may receive a job promotion, graduate from university with distinction, we may succeed in our chosen field, we may excel in any area of our life, yet we disregard these accomplishments. We certainly don't take pride in them. It 'doesn't really' count. We think it must be some sort of 'fluke' or error. We can live in fear for years with the thought, 'What if people find out I am not as good as they think I am?'

We can also be extremely creative and could offer much to ourselves, family, friends and employers in the way of creative ideas or strategies. Yet we don't voice them, because we are frightened that people will think we are stupid or silly. How many times have we come up with an idea or strategy and held it back? Then we find someone will come up with a similar idea a few months later, and it will be accepted and sometimes applauded for its originality and viability. All the while, we beat ourselves up because we cannot meet our expectations we have of our self!

Not accepting ourselves is not skilul, or compassionate and is a major violation of ourselves. Until we can accept ourselves as we are right now, we will be in continual conflict because we are trying to be someone other than we are. And this, as I have said, generates anxiety and depression.

It also impacts on our lives in other ways. When we don't accept ourselves we are unable to accept other people as they are. Although we may not be aware of it, we keep trying to 'change' ourselves to fit the image of who we think we should be, and we keep trying to change other people or wanting them to change, to fit the image of who we want them to be. This can and does create a great deal of underlying tension and conflict within our relationships.

We long for the 'happy ever after' with our partners, family members and friends. We think to ourselves, 'if I just try a bit harder' and if they 'just try a bit harder' to be who we want them to be, all our private and secret yearnings will be realised.

Perfectionism

From: Karen
SUBJECT: PERFECTIONISM
Vicki, you're right. It's perfectionism, and the belief that unless I'm perfect, I'm not good enough and I am not acceptable. I guess my self-esteem is low, so I believe I have to be perfect to be acceptable, because just being myself isn't good enough. I've been working on these issues for a little while now. Guess I'm still learning!

From: Janet
SUBJECT: PERFECTIONISM
I fully understand the perfectionism you speak of, Karen. Most of my early life I spent trying to please my parents. I was always criticised and never felt I was good enough. Later I always felt everything I did had to be perfect, the perfect wife, mother, cook, dressmaker.

One of the things that helped me when I started to take control of my panic disorder and agoraphobia was to take time out each day to look at the things I could do well, and not always be busting myself to do better. Also learning to accept praise and learning to have an opinion on things even if I kept it to myself.

I used to be proud of my perfectionism, now I hate what it has done to me. I still have to constantly ask myself, 'Does it really matter?'

From: Vicki

SUBJECT: PERFECTIONISM

Perfection is a trap. Whose idea of perfection are we working to? Where is the 'blue-print'. We may see role models we want to measure up to, but usually we have a distorted view of these role models, because we have only ever seen them at their best.

Perfectionism will always be a huge unattainable goal, because the goal-posts keep on being moved! A great substitute is 'to be the best I can'. You are then measuring yourself with your own values and not the values of other people. Let's face it, it is usually the combined values of every person you have ever met. And it is a tall order to live up to!

The first time I consciously let go of the 'need to be perfect', I was so thrilled. I didn't explode into a pile of dust as I thought I would. All I did was let my boss look for a lost phone number without offering to help. The perfect employee would have been able to fix it in a trice, without being asked, and I was always the perfect employee springing to the rescue.

This was something so simple. But boy, the freedom, the possibilities! It really didn't make me a lesser person, as I thought it would. Things have grown from there. I'm still good at my job, I just don't try to do the job of everyone else these days.

From: Group member

SUBJECT: PERFECTIONISM

This is what everybody is always expecting of us. But I find if I am trying to be more of a perfectionist, then I am never happy with what I have produced by the end of it. It is always 'It could have been better. I should have started it earlier and spent more time on it. This is not quite what I wanted it to be, but it will have to do.'

Why does everyone expect us to be a perfectionist? If we become mindful, we will realise it is more that we expect ourselves to be perfect. And we do so because we don't accept ourselves, so we feel we just have to keep on trying harder and harder to reach this idealised state. And we go round and round in circles trying to do this. As Vicki says, 'The goal-posts just keep on moving.'

Part of our lack of acceptance of ourselves means that we do not acknowledge, let alone accept, our intelligence, our skills and our creativity. We think we are stupid, we think we have to keep on trying to 'prove' ourselves and we worry that we will be exposed as frauds or explode in a 'pile of dust'! We are intelligent, we do have a great number of skills, we just don't recognise them!

So many people say to me, 'But what if people find out what I am really like?' What if we find out what we are really like? What if we find out we are intelligent? That we do indeed have many skills? And what if people do appreciate us for who we are, not who we think we should be? What then?

When we stop trying to be perfect we take away so much of the pressure we place on ourselves — and we will also find that we do not fail. In fact, we have much more energy to work more efficiently and productively, because we are not creating unnecessary stress or feeling guilty about 'what a terrible job' we did!

As I've said, our anxiety can become our teacher by showing us how we are violating and harming ourselves. When our anxiety points out the areas where we are doing this, we need to examine and question our beliefs about ourselves and who we think we should be. We need to see if they are relevant and necessary to us now, or if they are a carry-over from the past. If we decide these beliefs are no longer necessary to us, we can then choose to live our life in a different, more skilful way.

Growth anxiety

Choosing to live our life more skilfully means we begin to allow our emotional development to unfold. In doing so we 'disidentify' with the 'need to belong' level and begin working towards meeting our self-esteem needs. This means accepting ourselves and taking responsibility for ourselves. It means honouring our own needs and taking care of ourselves by setting boundaries where we need to.

And we may feel anxious as we begin to do this. But this anxiety is different. It is not 'anxiety disorder' anxiety, rather it is 'growth' anxiety. We are taking the first steps in becoming ourselves and it is natural and normal for us to feel this way. If we can allow the 'growth' anxiety to be there, and not contaminate it with thoughts of 'what will people think', then we will be able to move forward.

The more we practise skilful compassionate action, the more we see its simplicity, and in that simplicity is power and freedom. When we accept ourselves, we accept other people for who they are. When we take responsibility for our lives, we give back the responsibility to other people for their life. We can then contribute to other people and society in much healthier ways than we are able to now. The major contribution we can make in our lives, in the lives of other people and within society is for us to be truly ourselves.

From: Karen

SUBJECT: ANXIETY AS OUR TEACHER

I have found the whole key is to speak up early enough, to prevent anxiety in the first place.

I had been feeling a bit overstretched by our plans for a few days, but I didn't want to disappoint anybody, so I was just going to go along with it. No wonder I was feeling a bit antsy and cranky and, yes, a bit anxious. It was certainly a good lesson and an eye opener to see what happens when we stifle ourselves in order to be pleasing and nice.

Sometimes I think we feel as if the pressure is coming from outside of us, as if others are putting it upon us. When we really look at it though, we are putting the pressure on ourselves by saying 'yes', to too many things at once, trying to please, overstretching ourselves, and then telling ourselves we are bad, inadequate, rude or selfish if we don't follow through.

From: Margaret

SUBJECT: ANXIETY AS OUR TEACHER

I've been concentrating lately on using my anxiety as a tool so that I can work out what's making me anxious. Every time I get anxious, I've been stopping and thinking about where the anxiety is coming from and also writing down when I get anxious.

The interesting thing is I've been noticing that I get anxious in the middle of a conversation. I realise that I'm laughing when I don't think what the person is saying is funny. Or another time I was talking to someone about feeling a bit sad about a life change, and what the other person was saying made me feel like it was silly to be sad.

Then I realised that I wasn't being true to myself because I was denying my feelings and that's why I felt anxious. I can see the process working!!

I can truly see that I can use my anxiety to let me know what I really feel about a situation or whatever. I'm only just beginning with this, but I recommend it to everyone!! A few weeks ago I knew the theory but I just couldn't see how it could work. I'm excited.

CHAPTER 12

EXPOSED

From: Karen

SUBJECT: THERAPY

What I can't understand is why the therapists feel that talking about something that happened ten, twenty or even thirty years ago is actually going to help us now.

From: Bronwyn

SUBJECT: THERAPY

This type of therapy isn't going to help us learn to manage our panic and anxiety thinking. It isn't going to get us out of the house, into the supermarket, being able to drive again, or help us work through other forms of avoidance behaviour. This is what mindfulness, or other cognitive behavioral techniques do. But, from my experience, it is people who go into therapy after developing these skills who go through to full recovery and stay recovered. Of course, not everyone is going to want to do this, and this is part of what recovery is all about. Recognising and doing what we need to do for ourselves.

Mindfulness and cognitive therapy are targeted to our immediate situation, and teach us how to control and manage our panic and anxiety. This is the top layer of the 'onion'. But unlike cognitive therapy, working with meditation and a mindfulness technique can show us current or past personal issues that we do need to address, and psychotherapy can assist us with this. In fact, 'meditation may facilitate the psychotherapeutic process' (Task Force on Meditation 1977).

Psychotherapy is a two-way partnership between us and our therapist.

I see therapy working at two different levels. The first works with our knowledge of our childhood experiences. It looks at what happened to us as children. This may mean confronting our hurt, pain, anger, rage, grief and sadness, and learning not to be frightened by the power and intensity of these feelings. This is why it is so important for us to have a good working relationship with our therapist.

As we work with this, the second level of therapy comes into play and it involves issues of trust. I will come back to the second level in a moment. But, at the first level, it is our responsibility when we are in therapy to work through our emotions — not suppress them, run from them or deny them. It is also our responsibility to work all the way through and not give up part way, otherwise we can remain a victim of our past and present and nothing much changes in the future.

Therapy can be difficult, but it is all part of the process and it is worth it! Sometimes we may feel anxious and panicky. Our anxiety and panic can teach us to understand why we are feeling this way. We may be resisting something we don't want to face or deal with. We may break through and begin to see things as they really are. We could be getting in touch with our primary emotions and, because they are so strong, we become frightened.

These are the types of issues that our therapist can help us work through. And this brings us to the second and much more subtle part of therapy.

This second level deals not with what happened to us, but what we needed to do as children to feel loved and cared for. The second level of therapy applies to all of us, whether we come from an abusive background or not. We all adopted beliefs about ourselves and made decisions about who we should be based on these beliefs.

There is nothing wrong with this, but we have taken this to the extent that these belief systems and our decisions based on them are still keeping us trapped emotionally in the past. We don't realise how these belief systems and decisions impact on us right now, in every aspect of our life, nor how they create so much of our underlying anxiety and depression. Our belief systems have meant that we unwittingly betrayed the trust and respect we could have developed in ourselves.

This is the reason why we may know intellectually that our anxiety and panic won't hurt us, but why we can't feel the truth of this emotionally.

We don't trust ourselves or our intelligence. Mindfulness shows us how our thoughts create our fears and our symptoms. As we see this, we understand emotionally why our anxiety and panic won't hurt.

As we peel back the onion, mindfulness will also show us how we are violating our responsibility to our self and will show us that we do indeed have a choice in how we live our life. We can choose whether to change our belief systems or remain with the old one. If we choose to change, we do so by skilful compassionate action — accepting ourselves as we are and being responsible for ourselves.

This is why therapy can be important: it helps us to get in touch, not just with our own emotions but, at the second level, what we have unwittingly done to ourselves. Our therapist can assist us in seeing the choice, and supporting us as we begin to take responsibility for our lives and change our belief systems to healthier and more mature ones. Part of this means learning to trust ourselves and learning to trust our therapist.

We need a therapist who is non-judgmental. This enables us to learn to express our emotions and to change our belief systems in a non-judgmental and safe environment. If we decide to see one, then we need to choose our therapist carefully. We are not going to get anywhere if we have a therapist who:

- just sits there and stares, rarely saying anything;
- nods off to sleep during the session;
- holds the floor, talking of their life experience or what they did at the weekend.

If this happens, and unfortunately it can, we need to find another therapist. Some people will actually stay in a therapy situation like this because of misguided loyalty to the therapist: 'They must be tired. They just needed someone to talk to!'

If we have a therapist who helps us gain insight into the issues that concern us, but does nothing to help us to incorporate those insights into everyday living, then again we are not going to get very far. All we will have is a whole lot of insights and, probably, even more confused feelings. 'I understand, I realise it all now, but what can I do? Nothing has changed, so what is the point?'

It is our responsibility to work with our insights and change our perception and behaviour accordingly. And this can be done with assistance from our therapist. Sitting and talking, going round in circles about the same issues for years is not productive or healthy.

We may have a therapist who challenges us to bring our insights into everyday living, but we need to be responsible for ourselves and meet this challenge. If not, nothing much will change.

Other people will say to me, 'There is no point in being angry about my past. My therapist tells me I need to forgive everyone so I am trying to. But it doesn't take my panic, anxiety or my depression away.'

Nor will it, if we go straight from insight to forgiveness. Forgiveness is a four-step process:

1. insight;
2. anger and grief;
3. acceptance;
4. possible forgiveness.

I say 'possible' because some people, depending on individual circumstances or trauma, will find total forgiveness difficult. Trying to forgive is a bit like trying to love ourselves. It won't happen. All that 'trying' does is create further feelings of worthlessness and hopelessness, and we abuse ourselves because we feel there is something wrong with us because we can't forgive.

Forgiveness is more a process. It follows on from insight, anger, grief and acceptance. Acceptance means we have worked through the pain, anger and grief and these feelings no longer hold us 'hostage' to the past. In the case of childhood abuse, we also come to learn and know that we are not a 'bad' or 'evil' person and that we are not the cause of the abuse. Acceptance for all of us, irrespective of our childhood backgrounds, means that we can then move on with our life without bringing the past with us in such painful ways.

Some people will move on to forgiveness, other people will remain at the acceptance level. We need to do what is right for us. Either acceptance or forgiveness sets us free. But we need to work through the anger, pain and grief before we can do this. This is skilful compassionate action.

As I said above, therapy is a partnership between ourselves and our therapists. And, by working together, we can become free of the past and free to build our own future.

Group discussion: therapy

Group member When you get into the family issues and childhood, you see how certain situations and certain people worked together to help create this disorder within you. Then you get angry at them, angry at the situations.

Bronwyn *People and situations helped to create our belief systems, which over time trigger our disorder. As children, our belief systems formed in reaction to people and various situations. But we are adults now. And while being angry is healthy and assists us in letting go the pain and hurt, we need to see the core beliefs about ourselves and take the responsibility to change them.*

Vicki The responsibility for how we feel now as adults is ours. This is what we need to work on. Otherwise, we are pinning the control of how we feel onto someone else.

Group member Like everyone else has said in their emails, I am too nice to say how I feel about things to people. I am too nice to stop being there for everyone else. I am too nice to say no. I am too nice to complain. But this is killing me. I think I am beginning to see what is really at the core of all this anxiety and panic — anger and rage.

Bronwyn *We all know how good and nice we all are, and many of us know the damage this does. So why don't we change? Why can't we just be ourselves? Because we are not recognising or changing our core beliefs. These beliefs tell us that the expression of our emotions is inappropriate, and that people will not like us or love us if we feel these or express them. So we suppress them and they convert to anxiety and panic. Beneath our anxiety and panic is our anger and our rage about various events, past or current, and our anger and rage at having to be good, nice people!*

Group member I get these anger bursts and I am not sure where they come from. My new therapist wants to do role-playing. She also said she wants me to take a rubber bat and beat the walls. I had another one who gave me a stuffed toy and a set of crayons and paper and wanted me to play like a child. I know this may work for some people, but not for me. It is all too much.

Bronwyn *With the underlying anger and rage some of us have, the bat and the crayons would probably melt! It is interesting because cognitive therapy helps us to work with our thoughts and our disorder in a realistic way, yet this type of therapy is the opposite.*

It seems unrealistic to get us to go back and play at being the child. I'm sure it can trigger emotions, but it is not giving us 'space' to face these emotions as an adult, at an adult emotional level. In one way it could keep us trapped. 'This happened to me, I can't change, it is all their fault.' We could stay a victim to the past, rather than working through it. Can you ask your therapist if you can 'open it up' by talking about your issues instead of using the props?

Group member I am not sure who I am mad at. I have had some very stressful days with everyone in my life.

Bronwyn *So many of us needed to suppress our anger, but the anger is still there, it doesn't go away, and situations in our daily life can be similar to ones we experienced as children. These can trigger the current anger and the suppressed anger can also come through at the same time. We need to look and see what our anger is teaching us. We can then resolve it once and for all, and we may find we need to set a boundary to protect ourselves from similar situations in the future.*

Group member I just seem to be mad at everyone who doesn't understand this disorder, that includes family and friends. Maybe that's the answer. Them not understanding.

Bronwyn *It may well be, but it could also be a 'symptom' of how we felt when we were not understood when we were children. Similar situations in our adult life can trigger the original feelings and contaminate our current situation. We see their lack of understanding as another invalidation of ourselves — which it is — but we don't see at the adult level, why they don't understand.*

We don't understand our disorder, so how can anyone who hasn't had it understand? Instead of seeing their lack of understanding as being realistic, we go back to the feelings of invalidation we had when we were children, and we draw on these feelings and become angry.

Whereas as an adult we accept this is how it is. We do not need to be defined by other people's lack of understanding. We know what we are experiencing and we know how tough it is. We need to understand ourselves and not invalidate ourselves. When we can do this we will not be angry at other people's lack of understanding.

Group member I feel so anxious when I am around a couple of people. I know that I am not looking for approval from them, because I did reach the point where I did not care one way or the other. I knew what they thought of me and I knew there was nothing I could do to change their attitude towards me. When I let go of needing their approval, they changed their attitude towards me. Now they treat me like their long-lost friend. I can't bear the falseness of it all. It is sickly sweet and, as I said, I am anxious when I am around them.

Bronwyn *As a result of circumstances in our childhood and the messages we received back then, many of us have a belief that we are actually 'bad' people underneath. Now we are adults, when people disrespect us and/or are verbally abusive, it can bring up the anxiety and fear of 'being found out' how 'bad' we are that we had as children. Because of the way they treated you, you may be feeling 'found out' and this could be triggering thoughts which are triggering your anxiety.*

Or, If you are playing the game of the 'long-lost friend' now to keep them happy, you will be feeling anxious, because you are invalidating yourself. Can you see what your thoughts are when you know you will be seeing them? And also speak to your therapist about this, because there will be core beliefs involved in this.

Group member I saw my therapist today, and she said that often, when we start facing our fears, the emotions that have been covered over with anxiety and panic begin to surface. She said it's okay and to just let them happen. But I'm frightening myself with ideas that I will be an 'emotional mess' forever.

Vicki   We have been suppressing our emotions for so long. Letting them out is frightening because we are not used to feeling them. But they need to come out.

Once they surface, you work through them and then they are gone. They will not happen until you are ready, and they will come out at a pace that you can handle.

This is part of learning to trust the whole process of recovery and trusting ourselves. The trick is just to let them happen as your therapist said. Just sit with the emotions as they come. Don't try to justify, solve or reason with them. You will hold them to yourself for a longer time if you do. Just feel them, don't resist and they will ease. Letting yourself feel them is not the problem — the suppression of them is!

You'll feel as if you are on an emotional roller-coaster but it won't last. Make sure you keep talking with your therapist about this. Don't hold back anything from her. You will get through this and won't be an 'emotional mess' forever.

Bronwyn *You have more chance of being an 'emotional mess' forever, if you don't work with them as they arise! 'Emotional mess' in the sense of periods of anxiety, perhaps panic and depression!*

Group member I usually deal with one emotion at a time. Anxiety! I can't ever remember so many emotions coming at me, one after the other, in one day. Is this part of what is supposed to happen, or is it because I am getting better at identifying my emotions?

Group member 2 This is happening to me, too. I can't remember a time when I felt so many emotions in one day. I can go from feeling great, optimistic, happy, to angry, to rage, to anxious, to sadness, to crying and then back again and not necessarily in that order!

I think what's happening is, we have been so out of touch with our emotions and feelings for so long. We have just allowed ourselves to feel a very narrow range of feeling so that now, when we are opening up again, reconnecting to our self and our emotions, it feels strange.

We're not used to feelings. We fear them and that's why we have suppressed them for so long. As we are losing our fear, we are letting them come up and it can feel like an emotional roller-coaster.

This part of recovery is really scary for me, because emotions are so difficult for me. I have a fear of depression because I was sad and crying, then I fear I am manic because I felt happy and excited. I'm only now starting to learn that these emotions are normal and human, and they are only uncomfortable for me because I had shut them down. I'd say the fact that we are feeling all these emotions is a very good sign.

Bronwyn *Exactly right! This is where it is important we talk about our feelings, express them and work with them with the support of our therapists. We need to be totally open and honest with ourselves and our therapists. Letting ourselves work through this and letting ourselves feel our emotions is skilful compassion in action!*

Group member I am so scared that if I start crying I will never stop so I hold myself back, but it is getting harder and harder to do. Someone will say something nice to me, just look at me with kindness, and the tears come. I will see something on television and I start to cry. I don't know how much longer I can hold it back.

Bronwyn *It can be frightening because we do feel as if we will never stop crying. This in itself shows the depth and degree of the pain we are holding inside us. It shows so clearly how much we have suppressed our emotions. And these do need to be expressed, but be reassured you will stop crying once it has been released. You may then feel true sadness for a while. Not depression, but sadness. You can tell the difference between the two.*

True sadness has a poignancy to it. In a way (and this sounds really odd), the sadness is tinged with a feeling of beauty. When this happened to me I couldn't work it out, because the sadness had a beauty and a gracefulness about it, and I have never heard anyone speak about sadness in this way. Then a couple of years later, I read about a specific meditation practice which talks about fear, the everyday fears everyone has, and it also talks about anxiety. It says in part, 'Going beyond fear begins when we examine our fear, our anxiety . . . When we relax with our fear, we find sadness, which is calm and gentle . . . and perhaps romantic at the same time' (Trungpa 1986).

Many people with an anxiety disorder now say to me that this is exactly what they experience once they move beyond the fear. And in this sadness, the full strength and power of compassion arises. Speak with your therapist about your fear, and allow yourself to cry.

From: Karen

SUBJECT: ANGER AT MY THERAPIST

My therapist said one of the goals of therapy is to get in touch with and release past experiences. So I thought, okay, sounds good to me. But when I left his office, I barely had the door shut behind me, and I felt very angry. I felt discouraged. I felt like he just doesn't understand how it is for me. I felt that maybe he was wrong, and I was really never going to recover. I felt down and began to doubt the whole therapy process. I felt as if I'll never get out of this mess. So why on earth would I have such a reaction when I left the office? Is this self-sabotage? Am I afraid to recover?? How nuts is that!!??

From: Bronwyn

SUBJECT: ANGER AT MY THERAPIST

Yes, I think it is 'self-sabotage' but not in the way you mean it. And, no, you are not nuts! You are at one of the critical stages in the recovery process. The fear of recovery. I know we were talking about this in the group a couple of weeks ago and I think you also emailed about it. This fear is very real for most people.

Of course, we all want to recover, but recovery demands so much from us. All we want from recovery is for us to go back to who we were before our disorder developed, but we cannot go back. If we did, we would still be vulnerable to further anxiety disorder episodes because we would still have our 'foot on the brakes' of our emotional development.

We can only go forward and that means emotional growth with all the demands this implies to our self, our relationships, friendships and possibly our career. Recovery means change, and we fear change, because we are frightened of ourselves and what other people will think of us. The 'created self' tries to protect us from what it sees as a very threatening process and will try to impair our progress.

I know I harp on it, nag and pick, but this is why we really need to bring up our mindfulness skills. In the emails yesterday I spoke of becoming aware of and bringing up the real self, the integrated intellectual and emotional self. And we can only do this if we are aware of what we are thinking and how we are thinking.

Using your example: 'He said this is one of the goals of therapy, to get in touch with and then release past experiences. Okay. Sounds good to me.'

This is taking responsibility for yourself. The real you, who knows you need to do this, so you can deal with it. How did you feel when you thought this? Empowered?

'When I left, I barely had the door shut behind me and I felt very angry. I felt discouraged. I felt like he just doesn't understand how it is for me. I felt that maybe he was wrong, and I was really never going to recover. I felt down and began to doubt the whole therapy process. I felt as if I'll never get out of this mess.'

This is the 'anxiety disorder' you. This is the emotional part of our self that we have held back. How did you feel when you were thinking this? Disempowered?

We need to become aware as we move in and out of the 'real self' and the 'anxiety disorder self'. As part of the recovery process we all go through the experience of what I call the 'two selves'. When we are attaching to our panic and anxiety thoughts and being all things to all people, we will feel the 'anxiety disorder self'. The more mindful we become, the more we take responsibility for ourselves for our thoughts and actions, the more we will feel the 'real self'. As we learn to do this, we enable the emotional self to integrate with the intellectual self, and the more freedom and power we feel.

This is a critical stage in recovery, and it is so important for you to tell your therapist everything you are experiencing, including your anger towards him.

It is also very important to be very aware of when you move back into the anxiety disorder you. And it is also important to be aware of why you slipped back and then take back the responsibility for you!

P.S. It does get easier!!

Real self versus anxiety self

From: Margaret
SUBJECT: THE TWO OF US
I can actually sense the two people in me at once. I am the 'healthy me' with confidence and a sense of humour but at the same time I'm also the 'fearful me'. I've noticed it with other people in the group too. In some emails they sound confident, witty, 'together', and in others they sound frightened, confused, despairing. Hopefully, the confident one will surge to the top with all of us soon.

As the recovery process gains momentum we do begin to experience the 'two selves' and many of us find this very confusing. Often we are too scared to talk about it because we are frightened we will be diagnosed with yet another disorder. But the experience of the 'two selves' is part of the full recovery process. We need to be mindful of how we can move between these two ways of being, by our thoughts and perceptions.

The real self is the freedom and clarity we experience as a result of the growing emotional and intellectual integration. This state of being is very powerful and we feel the power it generates. We need to be aware of when we get caught up in the mind games again, and move back into the anxiety disorder self. We will feel disempowered and helpless.

This is when we need to be skilful and take back the responsibility for ourselves. When we do this, the feelings of freedom and clarity return and strengthen. This is the recovery process, and the more skilful we become the more we begin to trust it and ourselves.

People at this stage of recovery talk of the 'battle', the inner war they feel inside themselves. The anxiety disorder self throws every doubt, every fear, every symptom, every 'what if' it has at us. It is not going to give up the mind games easily. It has a vested interest in staying this way, because it 'protects' us from all we fear ourselves to be, or what we think we could become. This is yet another mind game called, 'Don't go there!'

The final layer

From: Eric
SUBJECT: FINAL OBSTACLE
I think I have stumbled upon an important obstacle towards my full recovery. I've realised I'm afraid of the real me, afraid to find out what I will be like, that I won't like me. I am afraid that I will turn out to be a nasty, selfish, uncaring person. This all must sound incredibly silly. Maybe it's that I'm afraid to step out of the anxiety disorder cage after all those years. I don't know for sure.

I will need to see this fear of finding out who I really am for what it is. Just thoughts which are trying to get me off track. The constructive thing is, thanks to my awareness skills, I noticed 'it all happening' without completely getting caught up into it, so there is space to deal with these feelings.

From: Bronwyn:

SUBJECT: FINAL OBSTACLE

Brilliant insight, Eric. And definitely not silly. This is the reason why people come so far in their recovery and then stop. This is the *big one*. This is the root fear. You have peeled away the final layer and you have exposed the primary fear — 'What if I am a bad, nasty person?' or 'What if I become a bad nasty person?' This fear is the driving force of all our thoughts, our beliefs and our need to be all things to all people.

I can say all the usual things to you, that you won't be and that this won't happen, but it isn't going to help much. What I will say is that the one thing we don't realise is that the real self is not nasty, bad, selfish, uncaring. But the only way you are going to know that you're not is for you to allow the process to unfold further. There is simply no other way around it.

This is a major breakthrough, because you have become aware of the unspoken 'truth' of what you have been living all these years — 'What if I am a nasty person?' I say 'truth' because, actually, it is not the truth. But it is the 'truth' to the child you were.

To work with this, look at the words 'nasty, selfish, uncaring'. You need to question this. How true is it?

- Why did the child that you were believe this?
- What was the child told?
- What 'messages' did you receive from your parents and others in relation to this?
- How many times were you told as a child that you were nasty, selfish and uncaring? Were these 'throwaway' lines, not meant to hurt, but to drive a point home?
- Were they said with intent?
- If so, what was the driving force, the personality, of the person/s who said this?
- What was their background?
- What were they projecting onto you?

You, as the adult, need to see and understand all the factors that formed the fear you have of your self. And you need to see all the reasons why this is not true.

When we were children, words like 'bad, nasty, selfish, uncaring' convinced us that we were all of these things. As children, we took these words to heart and we felt there was something fundamentally wrong with us. We still feel this. And the truth is there isn't. As I say in *Power over Panic*, we need to take the risk and find out for ourselves. There may be aspects of our self we may not like, but we don't have to act on them. If we understand them and how they developed, we can simply let them remain in consciousness as a 'potential'.

It comes back to choice. It is a matter of either staying where we are at this point, or feeling this fear and beginning the journey to get to know who we are. The more we practise skilful action, the more we realise that we are not a 'bad 'or 'nasty' person. We come to trust ourselves, and we become secure and safe within ourselves. In doing so we trust other people with who we are. The one quote that I really love comes from the Tibetan Buddhist tradition. Bravery is defined as 'not being afraid of who you are' (Trungpa 1986).

The more we become aware, the more we 'peel the onion'. From the outer layers of our 'loud' panic and anxiety thoughts, through to the more subtle thoughts of 'what will people think', until finally the root fear is exposed — 'What if I am or become a bad person?'

This always becomes the number one issue in the workshops and programs I run. People are frightened of becoming themselves. They are scared they will find out that they are 'bad, nasty' people. And they will be selfish and uncaring towards others. This is why the demands of the self-esteem, in Maslow's hierarchy of needs, is so frightening. At the 'need to belong' level, we don't see the bigger picture and we feel that, in taking care of ourselves and being responsible for ourselves, we are being selfish and uncaring — bad, nasty people.

The practice of compassionate action turns our beliefs about ourselves and other people upside down. We have been taught that compassion means giving selflessly, and in some instances people have been taught that their life must be one of selfless service to others. But we all need a sense of self before we 'give it away'!

Separation anxiety

Most of us know the loneliness and emptiness we feel inside ourselves. We can be with people we love, we can be in the most intimate of situations, but the loneliness and emptiness remains with us. Many of us go out of our way to avoid these feelings by filling up our days and nights with the million and one things we have to do.

We may be alone during the day while other family members are out, and we spend the time talking with others on the phone, or trying to fill our time in some form of communication with others. We find it difficult to sit and be with ourselves. When our anxiety disorder develops, our need to be with other people may increase ten-fold.

The loneliness we feel is the degree of separation we have from ourselves. In needing to belong, and in needing to be who we think we should be, we have abandoned and rejected ourselves. It is the ultimate separation anxiety.

So much of the emptiness and loneliness we feel inside is a direct result of our not accepting ourselves. We try to seek this acceptance through other people. Until we accept our self as we are right now, we will not be able to gain the confidence and the skills necessary to develop a more whole and healthy sense of self. Our sense of self will continue to depend on other people's opinions of us and on our trying to prove there isn't something fundamentally wrong with us.

Instead of spending our life trying to prove there isn't something 'wrong with us', we can learn to understand why there isn't. And we can do this through skilful compassionate action. We need to look at the reasons why we felt we needed to create a self that could fit in with who we perceived we needed to be.

The child that we were did this in response to a very natural and normal need to belong, to be loved and cared for. Now, as adults, we need to accept all the reasons that have brought us to this point in our life. Not with disdain, but with compassion. And when we accept ourselves as we are, we then have a direction. This will enable us to change the aspects of ourselves that we feel are necessary for our emotional development and growth. This is taking responsibility for ourselves and it is treating ourselves with respect and dignity. Skilful compassion in action!

From: Jill

SUBJECT: GETTING THERE

I feel I have been progressing along okay, but more with the intellectual under-standing than the emotional. I was thinking correctly with my head, but now I feel it emotionally, in a very positive way in my heart.

What I am getting at is, I really felt all that pain emotionally and I could just let it go. It is the same as Bronwyn said I needed to feel in the other situations I have been afraid of recently.

I feel like this is what taking back the power means to me. When you let go of that vice-like grip, almost nothing can hurt you. Five months ago I felt I didn't have much quality of life, but I can really see how bright the future is and just how far we can all go.

CHAPTER 13

THE BEGINNING

From: Karen

SUBJECT: WHERE IS IT?

The funny thing is that, without the anxiety, I feel weird. It's like something is missing. It's almost an emptiness or something. I'm kind of looking for it, but not in a fearful way. More like, 'Hey, where is it? Shouldn't I be feeling anxious?' Is that common?

From: Bronwyn

SUBJECT: WHERE IS IT?

Oh yes. This can make people anxious and some people do panic because they don't understand what is happening to them. Just be in the 'weirdness'. See what it is telling you.

From: Karen

SUBJECT: WHERE IS IT?

It is a feeling of 'who am I?' I know I've done a lot of changing on many levels and suddenly I feel very strange, almost as if I have no way to define myself. I am not sure who I am anymore. I feel disconnected from my life as I thought I knew it. It's as if I'm beginning to relate to myself and my surroundings, my family and friends, on a completely different level and it feels 'wrong'. It doesn't feel like me.

I'm not who I was before the disorder, and now I'm not even the 'disordered' person. I feel as if I have no personality, no 'me' to speak of. I feel like I have one foot in 'anxiety disorder land' and one foot in 'recovery land', but why is recovery lonely and scary? Why don't I feel like me? What's going on here? Is this feeling part of recovery?

From: Vicki
SUBJECT: WHERE IS IT?

Feeling this way is not wrong, it's just different. You have reached what Bronwyn calls 'no man's land'. The place that seems like a nothingness. This is the space into which the 'real you' will fully emerge, now that the 'created you' is moving out.

This is a very unfamiliar feeling for all of us. Once again, just sit with it. Let it be there, and over the next few weeks you will begin to notice how to fill this space.

A little clue I can give you is to begin to follow every intuitive feeling you have. This is where I started to do things I'd always wanted to, but thought I couldn't, or thought it was silly. This included learning Italian, astronomy, even the Internet! I even started hunting out poetry I had enjoyed years ago. Some things you will let go of, anxiety may sneak in from time to time, but also some things will give you great joy.

Trust your intuition as it will be making itself more noticeable now. This is the real you, and your intuition will teach you about you, and all you can become.

From: Bronwyn
SUBJECT: WHERE IS IT?

Vicki is right. You are in 'no man's land' but, at the moment, you are looking at recovery from anxiety disorder land. Trying to see recovery from this level is like trying to see San Francisco from Alcatraz on a heavy fog day. You simply don't see the bigger picture. And the fog will lift when you begin to explore you and get to know you.

The first part of recovery is 'peeling the onion' layer by layer. As we do, we peel away our outmoded beliefs and ways of being. And we do reach 'no man's land'.

This final stage of recovery is the rebuilding process. We have dismantled so much of our previous ways of being, and now we can rebuild on the much stronger foundations of our real self.

Dorothy in the *Wizard of Oz* always had the power to come home. She just didn't realise it. You have already doused the wicked witch of the west and these final fears are just as dissolvable. Like Dorothy, you have the power to come home.

Follow your intuition. As our anxiety was our teacher, now in the rebuilding stage our intuition becomes our teacher. Listen to it and it will guide you wisely as it teaches and shows you how to become all you could be.

No man's land

As we begin to move into the final stage of recovery it does feel 'weird'. It's not how we imagine recovery to be. During the recovery process we have periods of freedom and clarity and they are empowering and uplifting, and they show the promise and joy of full recovery. And we learn to sustain these periods by resolving the inner conflicts of who we think we should be. And one day we suddenly find ourselves in 'no man's land'. There is neither panic and anxiety nor freedom and clarity. We lose our identification of both ways of being. Suddenly, we are a stranger to ourselves. We are no longer the 'disordered' person, as Karen says, and we no longer identify ourselves through the perceptions and expectations of ourselves and other people.

No man's land doesn't need to be frightening. When we understand it, it becomes exciting! I spoke of Maslow's hierarchy of needs in Chapter 11 and of the process of our ongoing development. As we practise skilful action and take responsibility for ourselves, we begin to dis-identify with the 'need to belong' level and we begin to move to the next level of development, which is meeting our self-esteem needs.

No man's land is the gap between these two levels. No man's land is a period of consolidation of the integration of the intellectual and emotional self. We are no longer divided by our internal conflicts of who we should be and of other people's perceptions and expectations of us. Paraphrasing Ken Wilber (Wilber 1996), we have 'dis-identified' with the 'need to belong' level but we have not yet stablised at the self-esteem level. But we can. This is the final part of the full recovery process.

We peel the various layers of the onion so that we can disengage all the various factors that generate our anxiety, panic and depression. And the final piece of the jigsaw puzzle falls into place when we recognise the root fear and dissolve this too with skilful action. As we do, we step off the rung of the 'need to belong' level.

Rebuilding

Throughout the recovery process we have been developing the skills of compassion, self-responsibility and self-acceptance. As we do this, we are beginning to meet our needs at the self-esteem level. As we step off the ladder at the 'need to belong' level, we already have the key components of the self-esteem level in place. Now we need to get to know who we are so that we can fully identify with this next level of 'being'. As Ken Wilber writes, 'The interior world, for the first time, opens up before the mind's eye; psychological space becomes a new and exciting train' (Wilber 1996).

This stage of recovery, as I said to Karen, is exciting, and the possibilities of who we can become are limitless. We are a 'blank canvas' and we get to choose what we paint and what colours we use!

We can, as Vicki suggests, experiment and try all the things we have wanted to do throughout our life, but have felt frightened of doing because of what other people may think. Some of our ideas and desires we will let go, but others will take their place. Many of us are truly creative people. All the energy we have been using throughout our life to keep the real self suppressed is now free. And we can use this energy to create a life we once only imagined.

Intuition

We will become much more aware of our intuition and, if we listen to its gentle voice, it will teach us and show us who we can become. How many times during our life have we ignored the quiet whisperings of self, which has always been trying to show and teach us how we can be? Our anxiety disorder is more like the primal scream, shaking us to the very core, in an effort to make us take notice. And when we reach no man's land we again feel the gentle whisperings of the real self.

Philosopher Paul Brunton comments:

The intuitively governed mind is an undivided mind. It does not have to choose . . . or accept one or two alternatives. It does not suffer from being swayed this way and that by conflicting evidence, contradictory emotions or hesitant judgments.

Skilful compassionate action resolves our inner conflicts, and our emotional development integrates with that of our intellectual development. Learning to listen and work with our intuition is the surest and safest way of learning to become all we can be. We feel the unity of the 'undivided' mind in the power and freedom of recovery and we can live this freedom every day of our life.

We don't so much find happiness at the end of the rainbow. We are 'over the rainbow' and we find a life-sustaining joy in not being afraid of who we are.

From: Karen
SUBJECT: REFLECTIONS

It's been a little over a year and my life has changed dramatically in that time. I think my capacity for joy and happiness is much, much greater. I don't feel like I always have to be 'perfect' or acceptable anymore. I don't feel like I need everyone to like me. I would prefer for people to like me, but if they don't I really don't care anymore.

I don't feel like I have to hide my feelings or my true personality. I sing in the shower. If I'm happy, I show it. If I'm sad, I cry. If something is scaring me, I say so. Those are things I suppressed most of my life.

Mostly, I've really come to like and respect myself. It's so clear to me now why so many of us have low self-esteem. I think we feel like frauds, like liars. We are feeling one way inside, but project a completely different face to the world. How can we like ourselves when we know we are lying not only to others, but ultimately and most importantly to *ourselves*.

No wonder when someone likes us we immediately think, 'Yeah, but if you really knew me, you wouldn't like me.' Looking back on my life, it seems as if I was living under some grey cloud, keeping myself in check, always on the look out that I might do something or say something to embarrass myself, or blow my cover somehow. Now I feel so much freer and lighter.

There are still some things I haven't accomplished, such as flying. But the opportunity hasn't presented itself yet. Even so, I know when the time comes I will be nervous about it, maybe even a little anxious, but who cares? Who wouldn't be nervous about trying something new?

I think one of the things that has changed the most in the course of my recovery is that I've finally given myself permission to be human, to have fears and worries without feeling like I'm wrong for feeling that way.

I wanted to write this because I wanted to give you all an idea of what it looks like from the other side of panic disorder. In *Power over Panic*, Bronwyn says something about how what we get from recovery makes up for all the pain and hard work of the working-through process.

Guess what? That's an understatement. She's so incredibly right about that. So, work with those thoughts and get out there and challenge yourself, even if it seems too hard or too scary. Do it anyway. It can't kill you, you won't go crazy, and you can only recover as a result. With those odds, how can you not try??

CHAPTER 14

FROM: GROUP MEMBERS SUBJECT: TO THE READERS

From Vicki

In the mid-1990s, after suffering panic and anxiety for nearly twenty years, I had the great fortune to discover Bronwyn's workshops for people with anxiety disorders. From the very first information evening I went to, I knew I was onto something very important. Something that would make a difference. At last!

I found out I was not the *only* one who had panic anxiety. And, what's more, the other people in the group were as normal as people I saw every day. I began to realise that there was nothing dreadfully *wrong* with me.

For the first time panic and anxiety were explained to us in a logical, no nonsense way. A way that from then on allowed me to relax enough to take a close look at the things that were happening to me. To see their effect and to see the huge difference I could make to the way I felt, and effectively take back control of my life.

The many things I had learnt over the years to manage my anxiety actually began to make clear sense when viewed from the *Power over Panic* perspective.

My life these days has changed markedly. There is an ease and freedom that I had not ever thought was possible for me. Panic disorder is no longer an issue for me. It affected a huge part of my life, but it has proved to be a huge growth experience.

Once the process of panic disorder was understood and became manageable, I continued to look into those things that caused me anxiety on a day-to-day basis. The 'self issues' became the focus of my recovery and I feel that it is from this area that the greatest benefit came. The increase in self-esteem, that strong sense of 'self', enables a far more realistic view of everyday life and its circumstances. With this came that most precious sense of being a part of the 'everything' again.

In my daily work as moderator of the *Power over Panic* discussion group, I am privileged to see these same changes gradually taking place for more and more people. As they work through the principles in *Power over Panic* they learn to take back their own power.

If you choose to use the mindfulness principles, these same changes can also happen for you!

From Martha

I would be lying if I said that I am fully recovered. But I would also be lying if I said I didn't now believe that I could recover. However, recovery has taken on a new meaning. No longer do I hinge my progress on how far I can drive or what stores I can visit. Instead, I gauge my recovery by the confidence and peace that is slowly gaining a proper place in my life.

I am hopeful but cautious, simply because I know that I stand on a fine line, armed with knowledge from this program but still remembering the past, and its painful memories of fear and misery. I've learnt that it isn't easy to strip the bark from a tree. Instead, it's a process of peeling away the strips slowly and evenly, and being mindful of the new bark that soon will grow. And then trusting that a rebirth is possible but learning to have the patience to allow it grow.

When I first began this program I expected it to be just like all the rest, a few positive thoughts sprinkled about, breathing exercises interspersed with some relaxation theories and ideas. None of which I would practise because I'd already tried them all.

However, this book shared a new promise, one that wasn't miraculous in nature but written by someone who'd once suffered, and suffered just like me!

Of course, in the beginning I was suspicious, wondering if there was anyone out there who could help such a wreck as me. Because I was worse than everyone else. Nobody could possibly understand how wounded and rough the bark was that covered me. I thought nobody could understand how painful it was to be a broken tree.

You don't need to hear the details of my story because you have your own. We all do. We're all in this together, tens of million plus — flickering lights seen from above, frightened and feeling very much alone.

Each day I strip another layer of bark, one by one they peel away and fall to the ground. Every day the fear rears its head, as if to say frantically, 'You won't peel away all of me . . .' But now I reply with confidence that I will indeed, and beneath the rough surface is a calmer me, content with where I am for now, but looking forward to a new branch, autumn leaves, a smoother surface, but more importantly, a deeper rooted me.

From Karen

My experience with panic disorder and agoraphobia started at the age of seventeen, although I had no idea what was happening to me at the time. I never sought help and somehow 'felt better' on my own, managing to live a 'normal' although somewhat limited and sheltered life for the next twelve years.

Then, at the age of twenty-nine, after several years of prolonged and great stress, my panic disorder hit me with a vengeance. The best way to describe it was that I had a constant level of very high anxiety twenty-four hours a day, highlighted with two or three episodes of sheer panic daily. I lost weight. I couldn't sleep. I cried a lot. I feared for my sanity. I feared I would never regain the life I had known. I was terrified.

I sought help with a local psychologist who specialises in treating anxiety disorders. I was too afraid to take medication, so I went with CBT alone and began my long journey to recovery. I made some progress, but seemed to be trapped somehow. I recovered a bit and was feeling better, but was still nowhere near feeling comfortable and happy. Then, in January 2000, I found *Power over Panic*. From that point on, my recovery shifted into high gear and I was on my way.

I had all the fears and limitations most people with panic disorder and agoraphobia have. I was afraid I was crazy, afraid I was seriously ill with something the doctors just hadn't found. I was afraid to be alone, afraid

I would pass out. How embarrassed I would be! Afraid I would lose my mind, afraid I would somehow snap and lose control of myself in some way. I had trouble going out of the house by myself. I had trouble eating in restaurants, visiting friends, going to the store or going to the movies. Basically, just living a simple ordinary life was a challenge to me.

I felt dizzy all the time, shaky, and had pins and needles in my arms, my legs, even my face and scalp. I seemed to feel the heat much more, but also the cold, too. Actually, I seemed to feel everything more, as if someone had turned up the volume on all of my senses. My vision seemed funny, things were brighter, colours more intense and light bothered me. My hearing was also strange, and sometimes sounds seemed louder and irritating. When I walked, I felt as if I was walking on the deck of a boat on the ocean, and sometimes I felt like I was being pulled to one side.

I was tired a lot, and seemed to fatigue more easily than ever before. My emotions were all over the place, from feeling okay to feeling angry, then tearful, then okay again, then almost too happy or too excited. I was sure my life would never be the same and, thankfully, I was right! My life has not been the same. It's better than ever.

Writing this now, it's been almost a year to the day since I found *Power over Panic*. I'm nearly 100% recovered now. I say 'nearly 100%' because there are still a few things I haven't done yet that I would like to do, like flying and travelling. Other than that, I'm doing wonderfully.

I'm working again, involved with my friends again, and have even met a fantastic man and we're building a healthy, happy relationship. I'm eating in restaurants, going to the movies, attending classes, seeing my friends, going to parties, and basically living life again.

More importantly, I'm not suffering through these situations anymore. I'm enjoying myself. I'm not tolerating or 'getting through' social events, I'm involved in what's going on, I'm having fun. I still get a little anxious before a date or a party, but Bronwyn has taught me that everybody gets these anxious feelings and they are normal.

She's right. After the initial anxiety, excitement settles down, I feel fine and really enjoy myself. In the past, this initial anxiety would have me making excuses to stay home. I've missed out on so much by doing that. It's great to know I don't have to miss out on things anymore.

I'd like to share with you a few things I know really helped my recovery. I really needed to hear these things, and I needed to hear them often! It's very important that you believe you are not now, nor will you ever be, crazy. You will never lose control. You can and will recover. Having an anxiety disorder does not have to be a lifelong sentence. It is a temporary situation, something that needs work and some time, but it can be overcome.

The horrible feelings and fears, the scary 'crazy' thoughts, the sense of losing control are all harmless, empty threats. They do *not* ever happen. They are nightmares that don't come true. They are like fearsome guard dogs chasing us down, yet they have no teeth and can do us no real harm. If you can believe that, bring your thoughts back to these ideas again and again, your fears will soon lose all their power over you. You will gain your power and your life back.

Another important thing to keep in mind is that recovery takes some time and, yes, you do need to work at it. I know everybody wants to read a book and be recovered by the end of it. I wish it was that easy. Reading a book is the first step towards recovery, but you've got to implement and practise what you read. You've got to make recovery your top priority in your life.

Recovery is also not always fun, and you need to be willing to feel uncomfortable as you begin to put yourself back into the world, and into situations that you fear. For example, even if you are armed with your skills and have done a lot of work, the first time you go shopping alone, or go out to eat, you are going to feel uncomfortable.

You'll probably feel uncomfortable for quite some time. But you need to expect that and allow it, and see it as an opportunity to work with the thoughts and feelings that come up.

Recovery doesn't lie at home. I know sometimes, when we are starting to feel better, it's easier to remain in our safety zones, in our familiar surroundings with familiar people. After all, who wants to stir up feelings of anxiety again? Why not leave well enough alone for a while? But there comes a time when you need to take action and get out there and face down your fears.

I know you will think there will be a better time to do it, a time when you are more ready, or feeling stronger, a time when you have less stress in your life. There's no such time, and if you wait for it you will wait your life away. You've got to get out there and do it now. Naturally, you don't have to jump on a plane to the other side of the world, but you do have to take steps. For example, if you are afraid to drive your car, get out there and sit in the driveway behind the wheel. It's a small step but it's leading you towards your goal. You need to take action. Often.

I'm now beginning to live my life the way I believe I was meant to live it. The anxiety disorder was like a costume I wore, a role I played while the true me was underneath the whole time, too afraid to come out. Thanks to Bronwyn, my therapist and some hard work, I've learnt to take off the costume and face my life with courage and strength, knowing that no matter what happens, no matter what crosses my path, even if I *do* feel anxious or panicky, I'll be fine, I can handle it. Knowing that has set me free. You can be free, too.

From Angie

Power over Panic has changed my life in ways I never dreamt were possible. I started using the book fifteen months ago. At that time I could barely do anything. I would have a panic attack just driving to the grocery store, which is a few kilometres from my home. I had a hard time going shopping even if I was with someone. I was in an almost constant state of panic and anxiety. I started using the techniques Bronwyn describes in her book and I started meditating regularly, and slowly I began to recover. I don't think twice about going to the grocery store now and shopping is fun again.

Recovery is a process, and it depends on your willingness to do the work. I remember asking Bronwyn, 'How long does it take to recover?' She said, 'It takes as long as it takes.' This is so true. I have taken three steps forward and two steps backward, over and over again. But I have never gone back to where I started, because I am learning so much along the way.

The most wonderful part of this journey is the process of getting to know yourself, the real you. The 'you' that was hidden beneath layers of hurt and guilt and self-denial. As you begin to peel away the layers, you learn to like yourself, then you learn to love yourself and, finally, you learn to trust yourself, and that is a wonderful feeling. You learn that you have the power to recover from this disorder.

Be prepared to meet the real you. Be prepared to face your fears and realise that is what they are. Just fears. Just an illusion. The journey to recovery takes a lot of work but it is worth every bit of effort you put into it. I am still recovering, but there is no doubt in my mind that I will recover completely.

From Melony

I have read and reread *Power over Panic* several times and have found Bronwyn's ideas simple and easy to follow. It doesn't seem to matter how old you are, or how long you have had this disorder. I believe it is still possible to recover.

This book appealed to me because I already had a headful of complex thoughts which needed some simplification. The idea of 'being aware' of what I was thinking, and seeing the way the fear and anxious thoughts bring on a mixture of symptoms, has been a revelation to me. It is so simple but so true and, along with meditation, this has helped me let those anxious thoughts fly away.

I had panic attacks and generalised anxiety disorder for twenty-five years before I was finally diagnosed. I was given a a diagnosis of panic disorder but this was not treated for another five years. The doctor referred to the disorder as 'stress-related symptoms' and only offered me tranquillisers as a remedy.

I believe the longer you have this disorder, the smaller your comfort zone becomes, which in turn brings out the avoidance behaviour, agoraphobia. Putting the *Power over Panic* method into practice has helped increase those comfort zones, helped me to bring back the power into my life, and I am in control again.

Before I read the book, I had started to fear driving long distances away from home, especially with an overnight stop, because I was frightened of having a panic attack and not being able to handle it.

Well, a lot has happened since I read the book. I have had several driving trips lately of a total of 8000 kilometres. Who would have thought that five months ago? All because I took the time to meditate and focus on being aware of my negative and anxious thoughts!

From Jill

I developed panic disorder and agoraphobia fifteen years ago although I didn't know what I was experiencing. I was diagnosed eleven years later as having depression, as my doctors didn't know what was wrong either! Thankfully, now my therapist does. Working with my therapist and *Power over Panic*, I finally have the answer. Now I feel I have almost recovered but there are still a few things I want to accomplish.

These are my thoughts and some of the steps I took in the great journey towards recovery. And it is a great journey. Difficult at first but, with time and patience, it becomes a great and satisfying journey.

Really watch and pay attention to your thinking, and watch how your body responds. Learn to challenge these thoughts continually, until it gradually sinks in and becomes second nature. It is a bit like the learning the alphabet or multiplication tables by constant repetition.

Meditation can help you with this, as it teaches you to be aware. It does take time, and you need to be patient and kind with yourself while you are working this through.

Delete the words 'should', 'must' and 'have to' from your mind. These words create high anxiety for us because, if we feel we 'should', 'must', 'have to', then we are not able to do what is right for us and we will be anxious as a result.

A big breakthrough that I made was changing my thinking from 'What if I can't?' to 'What if I can?' I would then practise doing something I wanted to do and, although I was fearful, I was not forcing myself to do something that I 'had to do'.

Learn to trust in yourself again. Learn to realise how important you are as a person. As the recovery process progresses, you will learn so much more about yourself and you will learn what is right for you. Doing this, you will find you will be happy and at peace with yourself. Actually, you will feel better than you've ever done before.

The last twelve months of the recovery process has truly been the best and most rewarding part of my life. For me and my sense of self-worth!

We all have much more to look forward to.

From Margaret

I've experienced general anxiety and social phobia since I was about twenty. I'm now forty-five.

My first panic attack occurred about six years ago, and after a couple more attacks I lost confidence and briefly became housebound. Luckily, I'd read about anxiety, so I had a bit of an idea of what was happening to me. A friend suggested I contact our local anxiety disorder association and they referred me to a psychologist. I also bought Bronwyn's first book *Anxiety Attack — Don't Panic*.

Soon after this I took up regular meditation which I have practised ever since. Gradually, over the next two years or so, my anxiety levels dropped and I had fewer panic attacks. However, I was conscious that my confidence level hadn't returned to what it was prior to my first panic attack.

About eight months ago I became aware that my anxiety level was rising and I felt like I needed some help. Luckily, a friend told me that there was someone who knew about anxiety living nearby, so I rang the number and found myself talking to Bronwyn!

Since then I have been working with Bronwyn using her book *Power over Panic*. A big breakthrough for me was applying the skills I have learnt in meditation to my daily life. Instead of trying to beat off my anxious thoughts using 'positive thinking', I have learnt to acknowledge them but not connect with them. I have also found the practice of 'controlling my thinking' invaluable; realising that my thoughts create the fear and that they are within my control, not the other way around as many of us think!

The next big hurdle for me is learning to say 'So what!' to my anxiety. I have made some headway with this recently and am working on my self-esteem. I feel optimistic about my recovery and I really believe that, had it not been for my anxiety and panic attacks, I would never have spent the time and energy getting to know the 'real me'.

From Lorrie

I had panic disorder for years and my life was very restricted through agoraphobia. I would have temporary 'recoveries', then relapse, and I could never work out why. Now I realise it was because I was not using any cognitive techniques. I was using distracting techniques and, of course, when the distractions ran out, I was still left with my old way of thinking.

I joined a support group and we were all taught cognitive behavioural therapy, but I was still scared of my attacks and anxiety. I knew the way out of my disorder was for me to lose the fear of my attacks, but I just couldn't get to that point. I knew that I was not going to die or go insane, but I was afraid that my attacks would not stop when I was away from home. I also didn't want to face the extreme levels of anxiety. I live in the country and so it took me a minimum of two hours round trip for me to go anywhere. But even setting up a graded exposure program around this didn't help me lose my fear.

I knew people could fully recover from the disorder, and I truly believed that I could also, but I knew I was missing something, some link that could help me do this. I spoke with the support group leaders and they told me that I was further along the recovery path than they were, and that I should just be content with where I was. But I didn't want to be content! I wanted more!

I met Bronwyn through her website and began to use her mindfulness technique. One of the most important things I have learnt during this process is that I have a choice. In the past this didn't even seem like a possibility. I mean, how do you choose not to panic when you are having an attack, and how do you choose not to be anxious! Well, I learnt how to through mindfulness. It is so freeing. I know that, like other people, I will still have an occasional attack, but it is my choice whether or not I panic or become anxious about it. Obviously, I choose not to! LOL!

Another important thing I learnt is that there is *no big one* lurking in the shadows. We've all experienced it at its worst, and we are not going to die or go insane through our attacks.

I know this is going to sound odd but, looking back at it all, you realise you are so much better for it. I wouldn't trade it for anything now. Yes, I hated it and wouldn't wish it on anyone. But I truly believe I could never have become the person I am today (who I actually like, by the way, LOL) if it wasn't for the personal growth that came about through working on my disorder.

From Eric

I am forty-one years old and my anxiety problems started over thirty years ago. They manifested primarily as obsessive compulsive disorder and general anxiety. Looking back, I can say that over the years everything continued to get worse until, two years ago, I acknowledged to myself that I had a real problem. I mean, I knew I had one, but there is a difference between just knowing and not wanting to face it, and acknowledging and wanting to do something about it!

I started to work with a therapist and everything started to change. One of the approaches my therapist uses is CBT. My OCD disappeared, but then I developed panic attacks. Looking back on this, it was more or less to be expected, since the causes of my anxiety were not gone. As I was just beginning the process of learning how to handle my anxiety, it found another way to manifest itself.

My therapist and I worked on, and I had a major breakthrough when I just 'felt', I 'knew', that meditation would be good for me. CBT had taught me that my anxiety was being created by my thoughts, and it seemed to me that meditation was the way to get to know and understand my thinking processes even more.

Several months later I came across *Power over Panic*. Bronwyn's approach was a major reassurance for me that I was on the right track. Since then my progress towards recovery is continuing steadily and the group has proved to be an invaluable support.

Of course, during recovery, setbacks are unavoidable and they are disheartening. I experienced one as a result of a major crisis in my employment and I held my 'ground' quite well, whereas two years ago I would have gone to pieces. I have learnt how to get through setbacks by recognising my thoughts and symptoms and dealing with them, instead of worrying about them. Not only that, now I get out of any setback in better shape than I was before I had one!

One of the most important things I learnt from *Power over Panic* is that attacks will not disappear completely for ever, but we learn to build our skills and ability to manage them. As a result, they bother us less and less until, in the end, they are nothing more than a minor nuisance, if anything at all! And I know that full recovery is within my reach and it is now only a matter of time.

From Janet

I hope that my experiences may be of some help to you. I am sixty-five years of age and have suffered from anxiety most of my life. I remember it from when I was ten years old. Back then it was called 'attention seeking'.

Throughout my life I had bouts of anxiety and diarrhoea, and it became difficult to determine what was the cause and what was the effect. Deep down, I knew only I could change it, but didn't have the skills and there did not seem to be anyone who understood enough to help.

About ten years ago, it was suggested it could be stress but I wasn't offered any help. After a particularly bad episode, I had a colonoscopy. I thought I was going to die. I then spent three months under a naturopath. About six years later the panic attacks started with huge surges of heat, my clothes would be wet through, and I developed agoraphobia. I felt a terrible sense of being so alone. I had no life and was ruining my family's.

Over about a year I went to my local doctor, who was only young. He diagnosed my condition, and put me on mild medication which was discontinued when I reacted badly within a few days.

He sent me to a doctor specialising in stress management and also suggested Bronwyn's group may be able to help me. The specialist started me meditating, but did not help much in any other way. I also started to attend the anxiety group and received so much help from the group that I discontinued seeing the specialist. The relief of finding help and under-standing, and realising that so many other people were in the same boat was unbelievable.

I attended many of Bronwyn's classes for panic and anxiety and self-esteem. Going each week I found the need for support almost addictive and feared the times the classes might not be there. I rarely miss daily medita-tion. It is a very important part of my life.

It is about five years since I found help. I now live for each day. Not worrying about 'what was', 'what might be' or 'if only'. What a terrible waste of time and energy!

For me, self-esteem was the key. I had a fairly strict religious upbringing where anything you enjoyed was wrong, and you were expected to put everyone else before yourself. I was a people pleaser and a perfectionist. Now I try to work out what really matters.

Life is not perfect; I have the odd hiccup, usually in hot weather, but I search for a reason when the anxiety rises.

I would prefer not to have had the disorder but, having had it, there are some positive aspects. I have learnt so much about myself and life. I am a much better adjusted person and much easier to live with, and I have actually learnt to like myself and enjoy my own company. I know what I have and appreciate it.

There is no quick and easy solution. The process was long and constant, with many good and bad days. The peace and calm that I have gained is my reward. I wish each one of you success in your quest for a better life.

EPILOGUE

From Rossi

Anxiety has been my main struggle. But you know, you are holding on, and we all are, and working as well as we can at any particular point. Sometimes what makes me angry is that I've 'wasted' so much of my life having this anxiety disorder. And I can get totally absorbed in that anger.

Yet what is life, really? It's a process, not a performance. And there is absolutely nothing we can do to turn it back and do some of it again. So that's where I scrounge around for a bit of humility for myself and say, okay, that has been my life these past few years, and it hasn't been all bad, and all of it is taking me somewhere. What am I learning from this process?

Wow, so many things that I might not otherwise have focused on, about myself and others, acceptance above all, gentleness and self-observation. And the deep, deep joy I experience sometimes now when I am relaxed, present to the moment, in connection with someone or nature. Would I have known that depth of joy without the struggle I have had?

Surely, we don't achieve the deepest levels of love and joy without struggle of some kind in our life.

LIVING THROUGH WISDOM

If it were not for suffering
would the moments of joy seem so precious?
If it were not for the darkness
would the majesty of colour go unnoticed?
If it were not for icy winds
would the rapture of springtime's warm embrace still thrill us?
If it were not for pain, for heartache and despair
would we ever choose another way?

Carolyn Barker

BIBLIOGRAPHY

American Psychiatric Association 1994, *Diagnostic & Statistical Manual of Mental Disorders*, 4th edn, APA, Washington.

Arthur-Jones J. & Fox B. 1994, *Cross-cultural Comparisons of Panic Disorder*, Panic Anxiety Hub, Goolwa, SA.

Arthur-Jones J. & Fox B. 1997, *Treatment Needs of People with an Anxiety Disorder*, Panic Anxiety Disorder Association Inc., Adelaide, SA.

Australian Bureau of Statistics 1997, *Mental Health and Wellbeing: Profile of Adults*, ABS Catalogue No. 4326.0.

Benson H. 1975, *The Relaxation Response*, William Morrow, New York.

Brayley J., Bradshaw G. & Pols R. 1991, *Guidelines for the Prevention and Management of Benzodiazepine Dependence*, AGPS, Canberra.

British Medical Journal 1998, Editorial: Antidepressant discontinuation reactions, 316:1105–6.

Brunton P. 1988, *The Notebooks of Paul Brunton, Volume 14*, 'Inspiration and the Overself', Paul Brunton Philosophic Foundation, Larson Publication, New York.

Commission of Public Affairs and the Division of Public Affairs of the American Psychiatrists Association 1990, *Information Booklet on Anxiety Disorders*, APA, Washington.

Fewtrell W.D. & O'Connor K.P. 1988, 'Dizziness and depersonalisation', *Adv. Behav. Res. Ther.*, vol. 10, pp. 201–18.

Hafner J. 1986, *Marriage and Mental Illness*, Guilford Press, New York.

Kenardy J., Oei T.P.S., Ryan P. & Evans L. 1988, 'Attribution of panic attacks: patient perspective', *Journal of Anxiety Disorders*, vol. 2, pp. 243–51.

Knott V.J. 1990, 'Neuroelectrical activity related to panic disorder', *Progress in*

Neuro-psychpharmacology and Biological Psychiatry, 14, pp. 697–707; in McNally R.J. 1994, *Panic Disorder: A Critical Analysis*, Guilford Press, New York.

Maslow A. 1954, *Motivation and Personality*, Harper & Row; in Wilber K. 1990, *Eye to Eye: The Quest for the New Paradigm*, Shambhala Publications Inc., Boston.

Oswald I. 1962, *Sleeping and Waking: Physiology & Psychology*, Elsevier Publishing Company, Amsterdam.

Otto M.W. et al. 1994, 'Cognitive-behavioural treatment of panic disorder: considerations for the treatment of patients over the long term', *Psychiatric Annals*, 24:6.

Putman F.W. 1989, *Diagnosis & Treatment of Multiple Personality Disorder*, Guildford Press, New York.

Sheehan D. 1983, *The Anxiety Disease*, Charles Scribner's Sons, New York, p. 20.

Tart C.T. 1972, *Altered States of Consciousness*, Doubleday Anchor, New York.

Task Force on Meditation 1977, 'Position statement on meditation', *American Journal of Psychiatry* 134, p. 720; cited in Kutz et al. 1985, 'Dynamic psychotherapy, the relaxation response and mindfulness meditation', *American Journal of Psychiatry*, 142, pp. 1–7.

Trungpa C. 1986, *Shambhala — The Sacred Path of the Warrior*, Bantam Books, New York, p. 8.

Uhde T.W. 1994, *Principles and Practice of Sleep Medicine*, 2nd edn, WB Saunders & Co., Chap. 84.

Weekes C. 1992, *Self-help for your Nerves*, 28th edn, Angus & Robertson, Sydney.

Wilber K. 1996, *A Brief History of Everything*, Hill of Content Publishing, Melbourne.

FURTHER
INFORMATION

For further information and contact details of your local anxiety disorders association, visit the Panic Anxiety Hub's website:

http://www.panicattacks.com.au

or write to:

Panic Anxiety Hub
PO Box 516
Goolwa South Australia 5214

Bronwyn's workshop videos and a double cassette featuring a meditation tape designed for people with an anxiety disorder are available from the Panic Anxiety Hub.